The Bridge is Down!

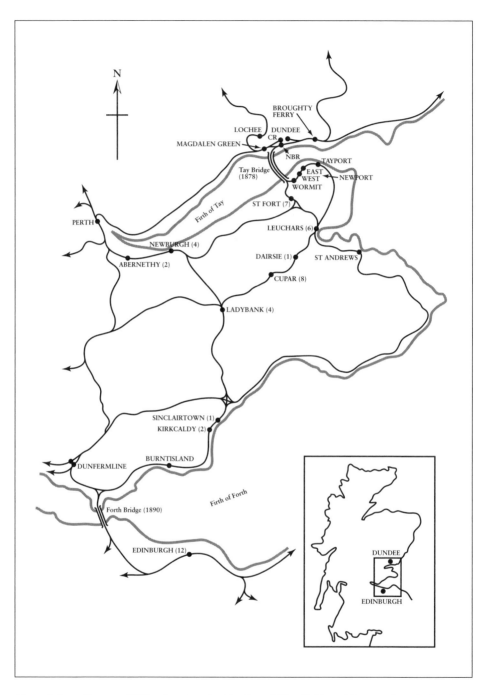

Map of the railways of Fife, showing the Forth and Tay Bridges. The numbers in brackets indicate where passengers began their journeys on 28 December 1879. In addition, there were nine passengers for whom this information is not known, and four train crew. The Forth Bridge was not opened until 1890; passengers travelling north in 1879 would have crossed the Forth by ferry.

The Bridge is Down!

Dramatic eye-witness accounts of the day the Tay Bridge went down, Sunday 28 December 1879

André Gren

• RAILWAY HERITAGE •
from
The NOSTALGIA Collection

About the author

Since working in the House of Commons for 12 years and studying for a doctorate on the foundation of Britain's railways, André Gren has written many articles on railway history, and a book on the foundation of Brunel's Great Western. He is now working on a study of the Gauge Commission, which brought Brunel's broad gauge to a premature end. He lives in Newbury with his wife, two sons and two Dalmatians.

First published in 2008

British Library Cataloguing in Publication Data

A catalogue record for this book is available from the British Library.

ISBN 978 1 85794 269 9

Silver Link Publishing Ltd
The Trundle
Ringstead Road
Great Addington
Kettering
Northants NN14 4BW

Tel/Fax: 01536 330588
email: sales@nostalgiacollection.com
Website: www.nostalgiacollection.com

Printed and bound in the Czech Republic

CONTENTS

ACKNOWLEDGEMENTS

None of those who are familiar with my working methods will begrudge Lesley Evans being singled out for special mention. She has helped enormously, as an editor, with illustrations, and in providing general encouragement.

I could not have done this book without the assistance of the Resources for the Blind and Dyslexic Service at the Bodleian Library in Oxford. I owe a debt to many volunteers who have freely read for me there, and to the heads of that organisation who have provided useful help in organising my workload on the book; they are Kim Miller, Paresh Raval, Adam Barnett and Eve Burgess.

Other editorial assistance has been provided by Sally Laurence Smyth, Steve Priestley and John Sykes. The book has also benefited from the critical scrutiny of my wife, Fiona. My Silver Link editor, Will Adams, has been extremely thorough and rigorous in his editing. The book is much better for the careful attention to it of all these people.

The struggle with technology that so assists and yet is such a bane to modern historians was aided by Harry Richards and Thomas Richards.

The illustrations for the book were provided by St Andrew's University, Dundee Central Library, the National Archives of Scotland, the Institute of Civil Engineers, the Science Museum, the National Railway Museum and the Strategic Rail Authority. Geremy Butler did the photographs of the train and the bridge from the centre of the Court of Inquiry's report. The task of getting them into this book also owes much to Elaine Seddon and Paul Kummer. Lastly, I have benefited from some good picture research in Dundee by Pete Twinam.

One secondary source has been so useful that it warrants being singled out in these acknowledgements. This is Murray Nicoll, Claire Nicoll and Grant Buttars's study of the people who died in the Tay Bridge disaster. It contains a wealth of detail that I have been able to use to bring out that this book is about real people, particularly my writing about the dead of the disaster.

INTRODUCTION: 'THE CIRCUMSTANCES ATTENDING THE ACCIDENT'

'There was a sudden bright flash of light, and in an instant there was total darkness. The tail-lamps of the train, the sparks, and the flash of light, had disappeared at the same instant.'

The world's longest railway bridge, the Tay Bridge, fell in a violent storm on the night of Sunday 28 December 1879. It took with it the 4.15pm train from Edinburgh to Dundee and all the 60 passengers and crew on board. This affront to Victorian engineering led to a public inquiry, or Court of Inquiry, into the causes of the fall. This book re-tells the story of the design, building, operations on and fall of the Tay Bridge, through edited accounts of evidence given by witnesses to the Court of Inquiry. The witnesses' accounts are arranged broadly chronologically to provide a sequential account of the bridge's construction, operation and fall, as heard by the Court of Inquiry.

The witnesses' evidence covered many aspects of the bridge's history. They included Sir Thomas Bouch, the engineer of the bridge; the inspectors of the Board of Trade who had passed the bridge as safe; observers of the weather on the day the bridge went down; train crew who drove over the bridge; the men who built the bridge; eye-witnesses of the fall; divers who went down to inspect the wreckage; and men who had been passengers crossing over the bridge in previous trains. Evidence was heard from several civil engineers as well as Bouch. The evidence of the passengers and crew of the last train to cross the bridge safely is also included.

Most of the evidence sessions took place within days of the bridge's fall, so that the evidence obtained was 'fresh' in the minds of witnesses. Nevertheless, there are a few minor inconsistencies in the evidence of different witnesses. However, the summaries here have not been altered to make them mutually consistent: they reflect the original words of the witnesses.

The Court of Inquiry's report was published on 30 June 1880, six months after the fall of the bridge. Its findings are summarised in Chapter 10. Its conclusions made stark reading for the bridge's designer, Sir Thomas Bouch:

> 'For the faults of design Sir Thomas Bouch is entirely responsible. For those of construction, he is principally to blame. For the faults of maintenance he is also principally to blame, in having neglected to maintain such a watch over the structure as its character imperatively demanded.'

Thomas Bouch was a prolific Victorian railway engineer, appearing before Parliamentary Committees 144 times during his lifetime, on Bills for railways for which he was the engineer. He first appeared in 1863, for three Bills. Almost all his work was in Scotland. He had trained under the famous railway engineer Joseph Locke (1805-60), who himself appeared before Select Committees on Bills for railways he engineered 378 times during his lifetime. Bouch also trained under John Errington (1806-62), who engineered a number of railways in England and Scotland, including the South Eastern & Hastings (1844), the Harrogate & Knaresborough (1844), the Glasgow, Garnkirk & Coatbridge (1840), and the Glasgow, Paisley & Greenock (1840). Bouch was the manager and engineer of the Edinburgh & Northern Railway (1845), for which he designed the world's first train-ferry, for use in crossing the rivers Forth and Tay.

Bouch gained a reputation for cheapness of construction, which often needed expensive remedial work later. Frank Beattie, an experienced railway contractor, referred to Bouch's success in 'having constructed the cheapest bridge in the world' over the River Tay. Nevertheless, on 24 March 1870 the chairman of the House of Commons Committee on the Tay Bridge Bill described the bridge line as 'an exceptionally expensive piece of railway'.

However, Bouch's brick and masonry viaducts stood well, notably Hownes Gill, Co Durham, and Smardale Gill in Cumbria. He also built two spectacular iron trestle viaducts at Deepdale and Belah on the Barnard Castle to Tebay line – the Belah Viaduct was almost double the height of the Tay Bridge. Bouch also built a viaduct over Bilston Glen, south of Edinburgh, which stood until the line was closed by Dr Beeching in the 1960s. Bouch's Esk Viaduct at Montrose, however, had to be partly rebuilt before opening.

Thomas Bouch was knighted by Queen Victoria for his work as engineer of the Tay Bridge shortly after she herself had crossed it in 1878. David Swinfen, in *The Fall of the Tay Bridge* (Edinburgh, 1998), records the visits of other celebrities who came to pay homage to Bouch's masterpiece. The Emperor of Brazil visited in July 1878, followed in September by Prince Leopold of the Belgians, who crossed the river on a ferry accompanied by Bouch and was taken out to the high girders on a wagon drawn by a ballast engine. The same month the President of the United States, Ulysses S. Grant, visited the bridge. Grant and his entourage were met at Tayport by James Cox, Provost of Dundee, and Edgar Gilkes, one of the managing directors of Messrs Hopkins, Gilkes & Co, of Middlesbrough, contractors for the bridge. Grant's visit on the tug *Excelsior* is marked by a plaque on the wall of one of the harbour buildings. They visited the training ship *Mars*, then went to Dundee for lunch before going to the bridge and walking out onto the structure. A possibly apocryphal tale records that Grant said 'it's a very long bridge.' The *Dundee Advertiser* of 1 September 1877 reported that Grant remarked on 'the singularly, substantial character of the work'.

In 1878 Bouch was working on plans for a bridge over the Forth estuary, but after the disaster he was replaced by Benjamin Baker and John Fowler, both civil engineers who had given evidence to the Tay Bridge inquiry.

The Tay Bridge's construction required 19,000 tons of wrought iron, 3,500 tons of cast iron, 70,000 tons of concrete, 10 million bricks and 3 million rivets; 660 men were employed throughout the construction, 20 of whom lost their lives. It cost £300,000 to build (around £17,500,000 at modern prices).

Charles Meik was Bouch's assistant, and as such was personally in possession of the plans of the Tay Bridge. He described the finished bridge as, as nearly as possible, 3,450 yards long, making it the longest bridge in the world at the time of its construction. It consisted of 85 spans carrying a single track for trains. Of the spans, three in the centre were through 'high girders', 27 feet high and 88 feet above the high water mark.

The bridge was officially opened on 31 May 1878 by ex-Provost James Cox, a prominent Dundee industrialist and director of the North British Railway Company, in which he held 200 shares. He had also been chairman of the Committee set up in Dundee to promote the building of the bridge. On the opening, a party of directors crossed in a train pulled by No 314 *Lochee*, an 0-4-2 tank engine built at Cowlairs in 1877, and withdrawn in 1925. Thomas Bouch travelled on the footplate of a pilot engine in front of *Lochee*.

Some impression of the beauty and novelty of the Tay Bridge can be gauged from a report by a correspondent of *The Times*, who wrote on 1 December 1879 that the bridge

> '...is so long, so lofty and so narrow that when seen from the heights above Newport it looks like a mere cable slung from shore to shore; and seeing a train puffing along it for the first time excited the kind of nervousness as must have been felt by those who watched Blondin crossing Niagara. Fragile as its appearance is, however, there is no doubt about its thorough stability.'

The *Dundee Advertiser*, however, was critical, despite the bridge's beauty, of the decision to make it a single-track structure. From a distance it would appear like a 'clothes line', like Blondin's tight-rope. Uncannily, the newspaper questioned whether, in the weather conditions of the Tay Estuary, a single-track bridge would be as stable as one carrying double tracks. The newspaper said that 'those who love something of the sensational in the way of adventure need only book themselves from Wormit to Dundee'.

The Times's confidence in the bridge's stability was, as we know, to be short-lived: only 19 months after opening, on 28 December 1879, during what was described by one contemporary as a hurricane, it was blown down. What went down in history as an engineering disaster, a severe blow to Victorian pride, was also a human tragedy; every man, woman and child on the fateful train perished that night.

The fall of the Tay Bridge led to a wide-ranging public Court of Inquiry into the causes of the disaster. The Court's three members were all engineers, William Barlow, Henry Rothery and Colonel William Yolland. Barlow, in addition to being a prominent Victorian railway engineer, was the current chairman of the Institution of Civil Engineers. Yolland's greatest work was engineering St Pancras station in London to the designs of Gilbert Scott. Rothery, the Chairman of the Court of Inquiry, was Commissioner of Wrecks.

The Court of Inquiry was set up by the Board of Trade on 31 December, only three days after the disaster. Its object was to conduct an investigation under the provision of the Regulation of Railways Act 1871 into the causes of and 'the circumstances attending an accident which took place on the railway bridge crossing the Firth of Tay, on the North British Railway on 28th December 1879'. The Court's report related that, after the appointment of the Court's members, they at once proceeded to Dundee for the purpose of making a personal inspection of the fallen bridge, and of examining any witnesses who could give evidence as to the circumstances attending the accident, while the facts were still fresh in their memories.

The Court of Inquiry opened on Saturday 3 January 1880, only five days after the bridge had gone down, and continued upon Monday 5 and Tuesday 6 January; Counsel appeared for the solicitor of the Board of Trade and for the North British Railway Company. The Court heard that a company had been formed to build a bridge, and an Act of Parliament obtained on 1 August 1870 for the purpose. A contract was entered into on 1 May 1871 with Messrs de Bergue & Co to undertake the work. However, in consequence of the illness of Charles de Bergue, the leading partner in the contracting firm, and his inability to attend to business, it became necessary to transfer the contract to other hands. This was accordingly done, and on 26 June 1874 another contract was entered into with Messrs Hopkins, Gilkes & Co of Middlesbrough to complete the work. The new contractors agreed to take over from Messrs de Bergue the whole of the existing staff and plant, as well as a foundry that had been erected at Wormit, near the southern end of the bridge, where a large portion of the castings required for the works were made.

After all the first group of witnesses had been examined and the bridge inspected, the Court of Inquiry adjourned the further hearing of the case in order to allow time to procure information relating to the bridge's construction and condition after its fall, principally from various railway engineers or civil engineers.

To assist this process, the Court of Inquiry appointed Henry Law, a member of the Institution of Civil Engineers, with directions to make a minute and careful examination of the bridge and to report fully thereon. His brief was also to report on the probable cause of the accident, and to select specimens of the cast and wrought iron, portions of the cross-bracing and its fastenings, and of the connecting bolts of the columns. These specimens were to be subjected to tests at Mr Kirkcaldy's iron foundry at Southwark.

The Court of Inquiry also called upon the railway company to furnish the particulars of the weight, strength and dimensions of the various parts of the structure. Photographs of the piers, of portions of the fallen girders and permanent way, and of the remains of the engine and carriages were ordered to be prepared and laid before the Court of Inquiry.

While waiting for Law's report, and for the answers of the railway company to the questions addressed to it, the Court of Inquiry was told that there were a number of witnesses at or near Dundee who could give important additional information as to the condition of the bridge before the accident. The Court of Inquiry accordingly returned to Dundee, and between 26 February and 3 March it examined a number of witnesses, mainly with reference to alleged defects of workmanship and inferior quality of materials used in the bridge, but also as to the speed at which trains crossed it.

Henry Law's report, dated 9 April, was received by the Court of Inquiry. Then, the answers from the railway company having been received and the case appearing to be otherwise ready for hearing, the Court of Inquiry was resumed at Westminster on Monday 19 April. By Saturday 8 May, when the Inquiry was brought to a close, all 102 witnesses had been examined; at that time some bodies still remained to be recovered.

1
THE TAY BRIDGE
GOES DOWN

*'The driver, David Mitchell, left a wife and
five children aged from 3 months to 8 years.'*

The Tay Bridge was built to carry the North British Railway over the
River Tay near Dundee, and its construction was authorised by Act of
Parliament in 1870. Only nine years later it was to be blown down into the
river it had been built to cross during what was described as 'a hurricane'.
A train was on the bridge at the time it went down: there were no survivors
of the bridge's fall.

That train was the 4.15pm from Edinburgh to Dundee, and it arrived on
time at St Fort station on the south side of the River Tay, where the tickets
of the passengers for Dundee were collected. There were 42 passengers for
Dundee, six for Broughty Ferry, five for Newport, two season-ticket
holders, the engine driver, stoker and guard of the train, and two other
railway personnel, making 60 persons in all. (Doubts over the numbers of
passengers on the train are considered in detail in the Postscript below.)

Counting from the engine, the train consisted of the following carriages:
one 3rd Class, one 1st Class, two 3rd Class, one 2nd Class and the guard's
van. After the accident the bodies and all the upper portions of the 2nd
Class carriage and the guard's van were found to be entirely destroyed.
Their lower frames were greatly damaged, and the axles of these vehicles,
as well as those of all the other carriages, were bent.

The train proceeded on its journey, leaving St Fort station at 7.08pm. On
approaching the signal cabin at the southern end of the bridge, the speed
was slackened to about 3 or 4 miles per hour to enable the engine driver to
take the baton or train staff, without which he was not allowed to cross the

bridge (the staff is now in Glasgow Transport Museum). This system ensured that there were never two trains on the bridge at the same time. When the baton had been collected, steam was again got up, and the train passed onto the bridge. The signalman, Thomas Barclay, signalled the fact to the north cabin. The time, according to the entry in his book, was exactly 13 minutes after 7 o'clock. It was then blowing a strong gale from west-south-west, and therefore almost directly at right-angles to the bridge. There was a full moon, but it was quite dark, owing to the face of the moon being obscured by clouds. However, the parting of the clouds meant that the full moon lit up the scene brightly from time to time.

John Watt, a surfaceman employed by the North British Railway Company, had gone to keep Barclay company and was in the cabin when the train passed; his evidence as an eye-witness is covered in Chapter 2. While Barclay was attending to his duties, entering the time in his book, and also making up the stove fire, Watt watched the train through the window in the cabin door, which looked north along the line. According to Watt, when the train had got about 200 yards from the cabin, he observed sparks flying from the wheels, and when they had continued for about 3 minutes, there was a sudden bright flash of light, and in an instant there was total darkness. The tail-lamps of the train, the sparks, and the flash of light, had disappeared at the same instant.

The train never reached the other side of the bridge. The watch of one of the victims, William Peebles, was found stopped at 7.27. Two days later, on the Tuesday, the train was found by divers, partly in the fourth and partly in the fifth spans from the south end of the bridge, so that although it had travelled some distance along the first set of continuous girders, it never reached their northern extremity. The engine and tender were found lying on their sides on the eastern girders. When the engine was recovered, it was found that its throttle-valve was fully open. There was no appearance of the brake having been put on. The conclusion to be drawn from these facts was that neither the driver nor fireman had any warning of the accident that took place that night.

The police records showed that 60 people in all had died, including the train crew, and 21 left behind spouses; 13 bodies have never been recovered. The first body was recovered on 29 December, the bridge having gone down just the day before This was Ann Cruickshanks, a 54-year-old maid from Edinburgh, housemaid to Lady Baxter from Kilmaron. The dead were initially brought to a makeshift mortuary at Dundee station for identification purposes. The last body to be recovered was on 27 March, and was that of William Robertson (not to be confused with the former

Provost of the same name whom we will meet later). This Robertson was a 21-year-old gasworks fireman who lived in Dundee. He had been travelling on the train with his brother, Alexander, whose body was recovered on 8 January 1880. The brothers' bodies were both identified by the same woman, a neighbour from Foundry St, Dundee.

The engine's driver was David Mitchell, aged 37, who lived in Dundee, at 89 Peddie Street. Mitchell was 5 feet 9 inches tall, a stout man, with brown hair, whiskers and moustache. He was wearing a blue pilot jacket, a tweed vest, white moleskin trousers, a tweed peaked cap, grey knitted drawers, and a shirt of grey wincey (a very durable cloth of linen and wool). He had been an engine driver for the North British Railway for 15 years before the accident.

Mitchell's body was recovered on 1 March 1880 between Tayport and Broughty Ferry, his remains having been spotted by passengers on a cruiser between those two ports. Mitchell left a wife and five children aged from 3 months to 8 years. Two months after the bridge had gone down, the harrowing task of identifying his body fell to his wife, Janet.

Mitchell's stoker or fireman was John Marshall, aged 24. He lived in Dundee, at 18 Hunter Street. Marshall was a single man. His body was recovered on 7 January 1880, east of the first broken pier, and was identified by his landlady. A silver watch chain, some keys and a small amount of cash were found on his body.

The guard was David McBeth, a 44-year-old single man, who lived at 46 Castle St, Dundee. He was a tall man with a dark complexion. His body was recovered on 13 January 1880, about 300 yards east of the third broken pier. A watch key, his guard's whistle, and a snuff box were found on his body. His watch had stopped at 7.15pm. His body was identified by his uncle.

The last crew member was Donald Murray, aged 49, the mail guard. Murray lived at 3 South Ellen St, Dundee, and was married with two children. He was wearing a uniform with a cap edged in gold lace. Murray had not been due to be working on the day of the disaster, but was asked to work in place of an absent colleague.

The last body recovered from the train was found on 27 April 1880, almost four months after the bridge had gone down. As already mentioned, 13 bodies have never been recovered, representing one-tenth of the men's bodies, but two-thirds of the women's bodies. This disproportion was possibly due to the women's bodies being more heavily weighed down by their dresses when waterlogged than were the men by their clothing.

Thirty-four of the 60 dead lived in Dundee, and almost all the others also lived in Scotland. The passenger who lived furthest from the Tay was John Scott of Baltimore in the United States of America. He had been born in Fife, and was a 30-year-old seaman then working on a ship from Hartlepool. Scott was in the area and travelling over the Tay Bridge to surprise relatives who did not know of his whereabouts. He was identified by his mother, Margaret Scott of Watson Street, Dundee, his body having been found by the diver Peter Harley on 23 January 1880.

The passenger who lived furthest away from the Tay in Great Britain was William Beynon, who lived in Cheltenham. He was a married 39-year-old photographer who had begun his journey in Edinburgh, and his body was recovered on 7 February 1880 near the shore about 200 yards west of Newport. It was observed floating in the water by a man walking along the beach. When brought ashore it was found to be in a much decomposed condition, although a local newspaper observed that he still had his false teeth in place. He was interred at Cheltenham Cemetery in a 'massive' oak coffin.

The train before the one that fell with the bridge had left Tayport at 5.50pm and crossed the bridge at 6.05pm. The accounts of that train's crew are set out in Chapter 8. The engine driver did not notice anything unusual in the travelling of this train, but the guard, Robert Shand, and two men who were with him, saw sparks coming from the wheels of the carriages. Shand put on his brake, and showed his red light, but it was not seen by the driver; Shand also examined his train at Dundee station after having crossed the bridge, but found nothing wrong.

2
EYE-WITNESS ACCOUNTS OF THE BRIDGE'S FALL

'I saw a part of the second girder going off, and then in a second or two I saw another lump going. I saw a blink of light, and the blink of light had cleared away.'

The Court of Inquiry took evidence from a number of people who had seen the events of the night of 28 December 1879 unfold. One eye-witness was William Robertson, the harbour-master and one-time Provost of Dundee, a position he had held for eight years. Additionally he gave evidence as a frequent passenger on the line and also because, in his capacity as harbour-master, he had superintended the diving operations at the wreck. The Court of Inquiry also examined the records he had kept of the speed of engines on the line with a view to assessing whether there was a culture of excess speed on the Tay Bridge line that might have contributed to the disaster (see Chapter 4).

On the day of the disaster it was high water at 2.30pm. Robertson was then at his office in the Customs House at the dock, and the weather was then moderate. Robertson decided to leave his office at about a quarter to six, intending to go to church after going home. The weather was blowing fresh by then; before he left the office the wind had increased very much, and he left about five minutes past six, with the wind blowing in gusts by then. Robertson had some difficulty in turning the corner at the tidal basin, which was rather an exposed place. After he got to the west end of the Custom House, he got the full force of the gale, which was very strong; this would have been about twenty minutes past six.

When Robertson got home he told his wife that she should not go out, as it was not safe. She had also intended to go to church, but Robertson went by himself. He had some struggle to get there, as it was blowing very hard, in squalls.

While Robertson was in church the squalls were very heavy at times. A little after 7 o'clock something very strange took place, as if the side of a building or the roofing or something had given way. It was like something rolling along the roof, as if something had been torn off or rolled along the roof just for a moment, although Robertson did not think anything had been torn off. There was a very furious gust of wind just at that time. Robertson knew it had been blowing hard before, but when that gust came he thought it was very bad indeed. For a time it stopped the congregation from hearing the minister's voice. Robertson also thought damage had been caused to the side of the building. While he was in church that noise was not repeated, but still the wind was blowing very hard at times, with gusts beating upon the church at intervals – he could hear the noise of it very well. He left the church as soon as the service was over.

Someone then told him that a train had been crossing the bridge. Robertson immediately went to the railway station where he found a number of gentlemen standing waiting to go across the bridge to Newport. However, nobody could get any information from anyone as to any accident, and the talk at that time was only a rumour that something had happened. It was not known at the railway station what, if anything, had happened.

Robertson did not think that any of the gentlemen knew about anything having happened to the bridge. Then a gentleman ran in to tell people at the station that the Edinburgh train had gone down with the bridge.

Being unable to get fuller information at the station, Robertson went with a colleague to his own observatory, where he had two very large telescopes and a weather-glass (but no instrument for testing wind pressure). When Robertson got into his observatory, he shut the lower doors to prevent any damage being done to the observatory, and opened the west window. The scene was occasionally illuminated by the moon when it broke through the racing clouds. His glass was generally placed looking down the river, not up, so he turned it round to the west window, and commenced observing from the north end of the bridge. He traced the line of the bridge up to a vessel's foremast, which interrupted his view. He moved the glass past the foremast, and saw that there was no bridge. He said to his colleague, 'There is no bridge now.' He then went to the south side of the bridge with the glass and traced it to where it was subsequently left standing, and said, 'The bridge is down.'

He had discovered that the part of the bridge that had been constructed high for the purpose of navigation was down. However, to make sure he sent to his house for his night-glasses. He then went to the Tay Ferries superintendent's office, thinking that he could get a look at the bridge from there, but nothing could be seen of it. Robertson and other men then went to the esplanade. There the thing was very plain: with the night-glasses they could see that the central sections of the longest bridge in the world, a triumph of Victorian engineering, had been blown down.

Robertson went to order a steam tug to be got ready to go up to the bridge, but unfortunately his men could not get her afloat, it then being low water. They had to wait, so he went back to the Tay Ferries office to get the superintendent to go out with a steamer. However, the superintendent had gone with the steamer to Newport. Robertson left word that if the weather became moderate enough they would go out when the steamer came back.

When the steamer did come back, Robertson went out with it. Thus at about 10 o'clock he left the Dundee side of the river to go to the scene of the disaster. The ferry steamer rounded the middle bank, and went as near to the bridge as was prudent. There he put out a boat, and was the first man into it, followed by one of the captains and two of the crew and a master-rigger. The boat got close to the bridge and was pulled up pretty nearly at the centre of where the bridge had gone down. Then the men pulled away to the north until they got underneath the first standing girder, then they came back south.

The men could see something hanging down. It was night-time, but it was clear. They then pulled alongside the piers on the west side. This was the more dangerous side, the wind being from that direction, but they could not pull on the east side for fear of getting foul of the debris, over which Robertson could see the water breaking, warning them to keep on the other side of the piers. The men went through the north piers, then came to the south. The sea was running very heavy.

Robertson did not see a single body floating about. He saw some pieces of wood he could have picked up, but there was no luggage or clothing, or anything of that kind. Robertson realised he was of no practical use to anybody or anything, so left the site.

He returned to the shore and spoke with Provost Brownlee and with Mr Cox, who was acting on behalf of the railway company. He arranged to have divers ready to go down to the wreckage of the bridge and train the next morning, and these divers worked at every possible opportunity from that point on.

Robertson was always out with his divers. He was in some measure superintending the diving operations, directing the places at which the barges were to be moored, and the places at which the men were to go down. Generally the diving operations were conducted in accordance with his orders, and to his satisfaction.

The first trace that the divers got of the train was on Wednesday afternoon, subsequent to their having found the girders of the bridge. One of the divers belonging to the harbour trustees came up, and said when he got on the barge, 'We've got something now.' He pointed to his line for Robertson's men to haul upon it, which they did. Robertson was afraid that the men would break the line, and he told them to stop as the tide had commenced to run pretty strong. He told another diver to go down and cut a piece off whatever it was. The diver said it was something like tarpaulin or cloth. Robertson said to him, 'Cut a bit off. Go down and bring a bit of it up. Let us see what it may be.'

The diver said he thought there was a carriage. He went down and when he came up there was fast to the line a piece of stuffing from a 1st Class carriage – blue cloth lining with hair stuffing. He had also cut off a piece of waxed floor cloth. It was not possible for the divers to go down again that day, and Robertson went home with the melancholy satisfaction that he had at last found a trace of the train. Nothing else was done that day.

The next day Robertson's men made fast a rope to the spot where the man had cut this stuff out, and when they went back they sent the diver John Fox down by this line. When he came up he told Robertson's men that he had been into the 1st Class carriage, but there was not anything in it.

William Robertson had therefore been one of the first people to realise that the bridge had gone down, and was one of the first men to supervise operations to try to ascertain what had happened.

James Roberts, another vital eye-witness, was a locomotive foreman at the Dundee section of the North British Railway, stationed at Dundee itself. His job was to transmit all orders from the superintendent to the engine-drivers, firemen, mechanics, and all connected with the Rolling Stock Department, and to see that the rolling stock was kept in good order.

At 6 o'clock in the evening of the bridge's fall Roberts was in the Dundee engine shed, seeing that the day and night shifts were being changed. He noticed that it was a very stormy night. Although the storm had not affected the engine sheds, he feared the doors being blown off their hinges, so stayed nearby to help the men barricade and secure the doors.

Roberts could not see the bridge from the shed he was working in that night. However, he got notice that something had gone wrong with the bridge while he was still at the shed. One of the signalmen sent for him and told him that he thought there was something wrong with the train, for it had been on the bridge for 35 minutes. Roberts knew that he meant the train that was coming up from Edinburgh. A minute or two afterwards he saw James Smith, the Station Master.

The two of them went to the cabin at the north end of the bridge in order to ascertain anything they could about the train. When they got there they spoke to the signalman, then made up their minds to go along the bridge. The signalman tested the instruments that communicated across the bridge and found that they would not work. The two men got to within 8 or 9 yards of the gap, and there they saw that a great part of the bridge had been carried away. It was still dark at that time, with the moon shaded now and then with clouds. Smith did not go quite so far as Roberts along the bridge.

Roberts saw water rushing out of the service-pipe that conveyed water across the river to Newport. When Roberts got further along he saw a part of the bridge – the rails – sloping down. The rails were not twisted, but quite straight, although they were bent downwards. He saw nothing projecting at the end of the bridge at an incline downward; he took no notice of anything but the two rails. He could not see the other end of the bridge, where it had first given way, but he saw a red light on the south side, which at first he thought was the train brought to a stand. Roberts subsequently inspected the bridge again, and found that the rails appeared to be in the same condition as he had seen them on the night the bridge went down, but he thought that they had been longer at that time – the same shape, but longer.

While Roberts was on the bridge he found the wind very high indeed, and he could only walk along it with great difficulty. The wind was so strong as to prevent him from proceeding at all had he not been under great anxiety to know what had happened. It was only that extreme anxiety that made him persist against the force of the wind. He did not feel the bridge shake while he was on it. The force of the wind made Smith turn back; Roberts thought that the other man was feeling giddiness in the head. Roberts's engines normally carried a red light, and he supposed this had been the light he had seen that night on the bridge.

Roberts came back from his position and joined Smith, and the two men returned from the bridge and went to the harbour-master to get a tug. Roberts found him at the boating shed at the end of the esplanade, looking at the bridge. The tug was not got out: the wind was too strong, and it was in any case low water at that time.

The engine pulling the train, 4-4-0 tender engine No 224, had come from the engine-shed at Burntisland, and Roberts had last seen it the day before.

It had then been in good order, as was the tender. The engine was a four-wheels-coupled bogie engine, with 6ft 6in driving wheels, 17-inch cylinders, and a 24-inch stroke. It was fitted with Westinghouse brakes and two hand brakes, and had been built for the North British Railway Company in 1871. The engine weighed 34 tons, and the tender 24 tons.

As locomotive foreman Roberts had attended to its necessary running repairs. The Saturday before its fateful journey over the Tay Bridge he had examined it and found it in perfect order. All North British engines were examined daily by a skilled mechanic, and one such, James Moyes, had reported the 'engine correct'.

Peter Barron was a 65-year-old carriage inspector employed by the Caledonian Railway. He lived at Dalgay House, on Blackness Road, overlooking the Tay Bridge, which was 200 yards from his house. On the night of Sunday 28 December 1879 one of the cairns of his chimney pots was blown off. Barron left the house to investigate, having to cling to gateposts to stop him being blown away. Barron saw clouds passing overhead, and in the light of the moon, when it was not obscured by clouds, he could easily see the whole length of the bridge, which he was looking down upon. Barron put a stone locker where the cairn had been blown out.

Uneasy at the stormy night, he went back inside and told his family that he was going to see what was happening to the bridge. He went out and saw that the bridge was down. He knew it was train time, so he crossed Blackness Road and observed the scene. After a second or two Barron saw the first or second girder fall into the river. He immediately became nervous and rubbed his eyes. He then looked behind, and saw another fall, then he saw a blink of light, which moved. He could not tell what the light was, but was sure it was on the northernmost part of the high girders. He saw the shimmer of the river and a long gap where the girders should have been.

The light had been blinking, and he only saw it for a second; he had seen it for such a short time that he could not even be sure of its colour, although he was sure it had been a clear light. He had not seen the light before the girder fell. What Barron saw then was a part of the second girder going off. A second or two later he saw another lump going, and just at the time he saw the southernmost part of the high girder he saw a blink of light. The moon was shining as clear as could be on the river, and he saw the large piers nearest to the girders from end to end. He saw the blink of light as the second bit of the girders parted.

Barron had been holding on to a post because of the strength of the wind; standing there, he had experienced the heaviest gust of the whole gale, so strong that it made him clutch the post to steady himself. He had been holding on to the post for only a very few seconds when he saw the bridge fall. He then held on for a few more seconds; he felt so stupefied by the horrible sight before him he could not be sure of the exact length of time. The whole sequence had taken, he supposed, only 13 seconds. He looked at his watch: it was 13 minutes past 7 o'clock. He stared at the scene for 3 or 4 seconds, then saw the whole abutment or the bricks of the pier-heads in the water.

Barron went into his house to tell his family what he had seen, and afterwards went to a neighbour, Henry Gourlay, an engineer and boat-builder. Gourlay could hardly credit it, and went out with Barron to the spot. It was rather dark, and Barron thought Gourlay could not see it. Then the moon broke out, and he saw the whole of the piers broken, minus the girders. Barron told Gourlay that he thought the train had been on the bridge, but Gourlay would not believe him. He said that if the train had been on the bridge, the bridge would have been all right, because there would have been additional weight to it.

Barron knew that it was the time when the train was due, and he had seen a light, which he thought was the light of the train. However, he had not seen the light fall into the river. Only 4 or 5 seconds had passed between the two falls, only the time it had taken him to rub his eyes in disbelief. Barron was seeing it as in daylight; such was the strength of the moon. He had seen the blink of light, perhaps three girders in length from the high girder, and it had disappeared when the upper girder fell. He could not tell whether it was lamp-light, but the moment that he saw it was going down it went out of his sight. He only saw it once; he thought it could have been the light of a lamp appearing for a short time then disappearing, but he saw it only for a second. However, he felt at the time and subsequently that something had been on the bridge. He felt it could have been the red light of the engine, but did not feel confident enough to say so unequivocally. That flash was the only light he saw on the bridge that night – he saw no light moving towards the water.

Barron thought the last train had crossed the bridge perhaps half an hour before it fell. He had distinctly seen a girder fall and, a second or two after, had seen another fall.

✦

Henry Gourlay was an engineer and boat-builder at Dundee, and also lived at Balgay House, the same house as Peter Barron. Gourlay remembered the night of the storm when Barron had called on him at about 8 o'clock and told him, 'The bridge is down,' and the two went out to see it. Gourlay felt very astonished and shocked by Barron's news. Barron gave few details and Gourlay asked for none: he simply went out with him to the point from which they could get the best view of the bridge. Gourlay simply crossed the road to look at the bridge. He knew that, from that point, assuming fair light, anything happening on the bridge would have been visible. However, he did not think it was a very good light that night: moonlight was only occasional due to the clouds. Nevertheless, when the clouds parted the moonlight enabled Gourlay to see the bridge clearly.

After a little time he made out that the bridge was down – that the centre girders were down. A minute later he saw what had happened to the bridge; he felt it had taken him so long because he did not want to believe that the bridge was down. However, after gazing fixedly on the spot for a minute, he concluded that it was not there. In the light he could not distinguish the first from any other girder, and could not distinguish minutely one part from the other, with clouds occasionally drifting across the moon. Gourlay was a good deal put out by Barron's statement that the bridge was down, as his neighbour was very much a reliable man. But in the intervals when the clouds cleared he could see what had happened, and as he fixed his attention on the bridge, only then did he feel certain that it was down.

George Clark had lived at Magdalen Green, opposite the north signal cabin of the Tay Bridge, for 30 years; his house was some 140 yards north of the cabin. He had during his life been out to Australia, and had been in Scotland some years as a merchant. He had been to sea a great deal, to China as well as Australia, and had sailed through the Indian Sea.

Clark's home was very exposed to any severe wind that blew, especially from the south-west, but the wind that night came from the west. He had not experienced so bad a storm in the time he had been living at Magdalen Green – the heaviest storm that he remembered had been in September 1859, when there had been more sea but not so much wind. The weather on the night of 28 December was something very exceptional, the heaviest storm that he had ever seen there.

Clark had much experience of heavy storms: he had seen a typhoon in China, which he thought had not been any worse than the storm on the Tay

Bridge. He thought that Sunday's storm had been a hurricane. Indeed, it was so unusual that he was looking out of his window to see its effect upon trains. From his window the bridge was to his right a little to the west of his house. He took up his position to look at the train a little after 7 o'clock – about 10 minutes past – and from there he saw the train at the bridge. He marked the light of the train advancing very distinctly and thought it had just got into the high girders, because there the lights became less distinct.

Clark's brother was in another room, and he called out to Clark, 'Look at the fire, the train is over the bridge, look at the fire!' Clark looked out immediately – his head was only turned away from the window for an instant – but he could not see any lights – it was all dark. Clark waited at the window for about a minute to see if the train passed. However, there was no sight of it again, so he ran up to the observatory at the top of his house, from where he could look right down upon the bridge. It was too dark for him to see anything, but he thought the train was on the curve, although he could not see the curve from the window. The gale was so strong that he could not even open his observatory's window to use his telescope to get a better view of the bridge.

Seeing nothing from his observatory, Clark took a pair of field-glasses and ran down to Magdalen Green to see the bridge. There he found James Black and some other men. He looked through his glasses towards the bridge, but there was too much spray blowing over the esplanade, and his glasses got wet. He entered North British Railway property behind the fence and shouted to the signalman at the north cabin. The man did not hear, so Clark went up the steps and called again – the wind was so strong that a man could not be heard more than 2 feet away. The signalman came out to Clark and his companion, and Clark tried to speak to him, but could not make him hear. The signalman came down the steps from the box, and Clark said to him, 'Where is the train?' He said that it had been on the bridge for some time.

Clark did not wait there, and ran as hard as he could to the station with James Black and another gentleman. They told the Station Master what they had seen. Clark did not wait in the station – when he saw that most questions were being put to Black, he ran to Captain Methven of the ferry boats, and told him what had happened.

Clark also went to see the harbour-master, William Robertson, at the Custom House, but he was not there. He saw him afterwards in the dock, and wanted to tell him so that he would be able to get a boat out when the wind went down – it was impossible then to get out in any steamer. By the time he got down to the Dock Office the light was better than before – the moon had come out. He could use the large telescope, which was a very fine glass, and then he could see that the bridge was down. The wind was still blowing very badly, though it had moderated a little; it was blowing in very heavy squalls, about every 7, 8 or 10 minutes. Between these squalls there was a very heavy gale, a constant gale, with periodical heavy squalls and a lull between them.

James Black was a wine merchant from Dundee who lived in a house on Magdalen Green, which faced the River Tay. Black had also observed the very heavy storm, and at 5 past 7 o'clock he left his home to observe its effects. The wind was blowing the water of the river into foam, and the river was running very high; the spray was going right over the north end of the bridge. Black walked eastwards to a spot 300 yards from the bridge, from where he saw a mass of fire fall from the east side of the bridge into the river.

The moon was shining when the clouds parted, so from time to time there was a fair light, but at other times it was dark. His immediate thought was that 'there is a train in the river'. He immediately ran across Magdalen Green south-east to Buckingham Point, where he got shelter by a big pier. The wind was very severe at that time and he looked at the river to see if he could see anything, but there was nothing but the noise of the wind. He thought he saw steam near the north end of the big girders; however, he was not confident he could distinguish between steam or spray caused by the dashing of the water – it could have been either, but he thought it was probably the former.

Black tried to attract the attention of the signalman at the north signal cabin, so ran over to the signal box. When he got there it took him several seconds to make himself heard over the noise – he was accompanied by George Clark, who went up a few steps and spoke to the signalman. Black shouted to him to come down, because there was a train on the bridge. The signalman told him that the Edinburgh train had been signalled as having entered on to the bridge 10 to 15 minutes before, but he had no idea where it was.

Black told him that he thought the train was in the river – he had seen something fall from the bridge, although he had not heard the slightest sound other than the noise of the wind. Black spoke to the signalman, then went with some others along the esplanade, which he found a very difficult journey on account of the wind. Black walked eastwards from the signal box to the North British station, and while Clark went to the harbour-master's office he went to the *Advertiser* office. Eventually he returned to his house, arriving about a quarter of an hour after his visit to the Station Master.

When Black arrived home the wind was not quite as high as before and the weather was brighter and clearer. He now had a full view of the bridge, and he saw that all the big girders were away. His house at Magdalen Green was much exposed to gales from west-south-west, but that night he thought the wind was pretty much westerly. In the 30 years he had been living at Magdalen Green he had never seen a worse storm.

The mass of fire Black had seen was between him and the north end of the big girders, where they joined the low girders. However, the storm was so bad that he could not distinguish the high girders from the lower ones. He had not seen any fire before he saw this mass of fire falling down. The bridge gave way very nearly in a south-west direction from Black, who was standing pretty much in line with the straight portion of the bridge. The mass of fire had come down gently, falling.

Alexander Maxwell was a mechanical engineer who lived with his father, also at Magdalen Green, immediately to the north side of the bow-string girders of the Tay Bridge. He remembered the great storm well, and noticed at about 10 minutes past 7 o'clock that the chandeliers of the room he was in were shaking. Then, dramatically, about five of the chimney cairns came down from the top of his house. He had friends in the house with him, one of whom suggested he should look out and see the bridge and what effect the gale might be having upon it.

Maxwell accordingly went to the windows, turned down the gas-lights in his house and looked out. The first thing that caught his attention was the signal light, a little to the north of the big girders. It was flickering. He thought that the lamp of the signal was on fire. Then almost at that moment, or shortly afterwards, he saw two lights of the engine coming on to the bridge, on the south side. Maxwell followed the lights closely on to the big girders.

Before the train reached that point Maxwell did not see any lights – no sparks or fire – near or about it, except the headlights of the engine itself. He did, however, see the danger signal on the south side of the bridge. When it got to the high girders Maxwell thought he saw the lights shaken. Before the engine came to the big girders he saw, as it were, flashes, as would be the effect of it passing the spars of the high girders. Then the light suddenly disappeared at about the third or fourth girder from the south side. At that moment Maxwell did not see any fire or light, but about a second or two afterwards there was a flash, about two girders in advance of the train. After that there was another light at about two girders, all coming towards the north. Then there was a third flash, roughly two girders towards the north side, in advance of the place at which he had last seen the lights of the train. He had a photograph that had been taken from his window, to give an idea of the angle at which he would have seen it.

All of these flashes started from the bridge downwards, towards the east. He did not, however, see anything like a dark body falling from the bridge into the river. About that moment a cloud had come over the moon, so he saw only the flashing lights. Shortly after that he used a powerful telescope he had, and discovered that there was a gap in the bridge. He had noticed this with his eyes before using the telescope, but, not believing it, had taken to the telescope, and was able to confirm that it was indeed so. He also saw the water escaping from the service pipe.

At the time of the flashes the wind seemed to be at about its highest point, and was coming in occasionally heavy gusts. A gust came immediately after the flashes. The first flash he had seen was about 2 seconds after he had lost sight of the headlights of the train; the last flash he saw was some 15 seconds later. The last of the four flashes was the brightest. The flashes were in succession, moving forwards towards the north end of the bridge, which he could see very distinctly.

Maxwell thought the flashes of light were rather too red for friction sparks. Two were two-coloured, two red, and he had never seen friction sparks so darkly coloured. He wondered if the flashes or sparks had lit the gas on the main pipe on the bridge, causing them to be a little darker in colour than they would have been without the gas. Maxwell later thought they were too dark to be sparks only from the breaking of the girders.

A further and still more dramatic eye-witness account came from John Watt, a North British Railway Company surfaceman. Watt had done that job for 12 years by the time of the Tay Bridge disaster, for some years in the Dundee district. His duties lay on the south side of the Tay Bridge, and included responsibility for examining the points of the bridge.

On the night of the disaster Watt went into Thomas Barclay's signal cabin at the south end of the bridge; he frequently passed time with Barclay there. He had been there about 10 minutes when a train passed, and Watt saw from the signal that it was from St Fort. The train slowed down for the driver to pick up the single-line baton, then from curiosity Watt watched the train after it passed Barclay's cabin. As he watched he was startled to see fire from the train while it was still running along the permanent way. It appeared to be coming from the wheels and consisted of many sparks rather than a continuous flame. He had only previously seen such a thing when the brakes of a train were on, but did not know if they had been applied on this occasion.

When Watt first saw the sparks the train was less than 200 yards from the cabin, and he continued to see them as far as the train went. Within 3 minutes of Watt first seeing the sparks, the train disappeared from his view, about three-quarters of a mile from the south cabin. By then the train had got onto the part of the bridge that spanned the navigable channel, the high girders. All three tail-lamps disappeared in a moment, having previously been in full view. In addition to the sparks and before the sudden disappearance of the tail-lamps, Watt noticed that there were great flashes of fire, greater flashes than those he had seen continuously before. There was one great flash of light, then the tail-lights disappeared.

Watt said to Barclay that there must be something wrong with the train – he thought she was over the bridge. However, Barclay thought that the fire and the tail-lamps disappearing so quickly was due to the train having gone onto the incline on the bridge. Watt did not agree. Barclay stood and looked for a few seconds – he was expecting to see the tail-lights reappear as the train got round the curve. As the train did not come into view, he tried his telegraph instruments to see whether he could communicate with the north cabin. None of them would work. Watt realised that there was something wrong with the bridge.

Watt had been watching the train as it went away from him, and he had kept his eye on it until it entirely disappeared. At the moment of its disappearance he had not heard any noise, any crashing of the bridge or crashing of the carriages or anything else. He had heard only the howling of the wind, and nothing of the train meeting its end in the water.

Barclay and Watt tried to walk out on the bridge to see whether the train had gone over. They did not walk very far – it was so stormy that Watt could not walk, and he deemed it not very safe to go further along the bridge given the state of the weather. It was blowing very heavy, and he had never before experienced similar heavy weather at the Tay Bridge. He therefore judged it prudent to turn back. Barclay and Watt then went down the Newport line to see if they could see anything of the bridge from the shore. When they got there they saw nothing – the moon was clouded over at first. They walked backwards and forwards to see if they could discover anything wrong with the bridge and, if so, what.

Ultimately they got a view of the bridge, and could see that there was a part of it gone. By now it was about 8 o'clock, and they saw that a great part of the bridge had disappeared. Watt had no idea that the train had gone with the bridge; he thought that the train had been blown off the rails and that it had taken the side of the bridge with it and had gone over. He never expected to find that the whole structure of the bridge had been carried away.

When Watt realised that a great part of the bridge had gone, he went to St Fort to give Mr Morris, the Station Master there, the information. However, when he got to the station he did not see Morris, only his wife. He therefore decided to go on to Leuchars, where he told the Station Master that the bridge was down, and the Station Master then telegraphed this information to Edinburgh. Watt told him of the strength of the wind, and that it had been blowing very hard against Barclay's cabin, which had little protection due to the rising ground and a projecting point a little to the west. The cabin had been shaking, he said, not much, just a sort of shaking as when great gusts of wind come. He had only been sitting in Barclay's cabin for about 10 minutes before the train passed, and all that time the wind had been blowing in gusts, which became more frequent. He connected the wind with the disappearance of the train – he thought it had been blown over.

Watt wondered what had caused the sparks and the great flash before the train disappeared. It appeared to him as if the carriages were scraping along the side of the girders, the friction producing the fire. At first he had thought the sparks had been produced by the application of the brakes; the fire, he observed, was to the east of the lamps, from the east-side wheels of the train, and it continued as far as he saw the train. It had begun when the train had passed the cabin, about 200 yards distant from him, and he knew that the bridge had given way about 900 yards from him.

When questioned, Watt said that he had observed other trains in darkness, but had never seen sparks coming from the wheels. He formed the opinion that with the wind blowing towards the east, the wheels had been hard upon the rail, causing the fire. He had previously seen sparks produced by a broken spring when the carriage body had come down upon the top of a wheel, and had observed that it had been a bright light, which soon became a flame. The light he had seen that night had been on a level with the rails, and after the train had gone about 900 yards he had seen the great flash, then it had disappeared altogether.

When the flash went out, everything was dark. There was no red light or anything. Watt had seen the flash while the train was still on the level of the permanent way, and had said to Barclay that he thought the red flash had been the train skirting the side of the girders. It could not be mistaken for the opening of the engine's firebox for the purpose of adding more fuel; it was a flame produced by the friction of the carriages against the side of the bridge. The flash did not last long, only just an instant.

3

CONTRACTORS AND PAINTERS: THE MEN WHO BUILT THE TAY BRIDGE

'Nothing that was not perfect, as far as they could make it by inspection and care, should be passed into the bridge.'

'Every column he saw with a lug burned on was cracked.'

'Repairs were painted over. This was done very frequently: the foreman knew this was going on.'

The 19th century saw a huge increase in demand for the construction of major civil engineering works. In the Great Western Railway area of Great Britain alone, for example, 40 different railway companies had been established in the decade to 1840, and this fuelled demand for civil engineers to an extent not previously experienced; consequently the numbers of civil engineers and contractors increased dramatically to meet this demand.

Edgar Gilkes had for many years been one of the managing directors of Messrs Hopkins, Gilkes & Co of Middlesbrough, and since 1842 he had been connected with the manufacturing and making of iron structures. He was a member of the firm at the time it entered into the contract for the completion of the Tay Bridge, which had previously been contracted for by the late Mr de Bergue. Bridge construction was a matter that Gilkes had himself personally paid attention to for many years. He had constructed many large bridges and viaducts, including the Belah and Deepdale viaducts, the one at Belah for Bouch. Deepdale Viaduct was different from that at Belah, in that it was on a curve while Belah was straight. The piers of Belah Viaduct were also a good deal taller than those at Deepdale.

Gilkes had also constructed a large number of smaller bridges from Bouch's designs, including Kingston Bridge and Kew Bridge in the London area, as well as the large recently completed bridge over the Wear at Sunderland, which had spans of some 300 feet. Gilkes had, under Henry Law's engineering, built the Albert and Victoria bridges in Windsor Great Park, and had constructed a good many bridges abroad, including two in Norway and one in the north of Russia.

The Tay Bridge contract was to execute the work to a schedule of prices. This meant that anything could be added, taken away or altered without interfering with the contract at all, provided that the work was executed in accordance with the established schedule of prices. A change in construction material for the bridge from brick to iron had taken place before Gilkes had begun his work, and it was after the time the contract came to Gilkes that one large caisson was adopted in place of two smaller ones (caissons were watertight casings used in the construction of bridge foundations in deep water).

✝

One of the men who worked for Gilkes was William Newcombe, of Montrose. He was one of the men who actually built the bridge, as the foreman erector of the high girders. He was a fitter by trade, and had been building bridges and blast furnaces since 1862. Newcombe worked at the Tay Bridge between February 1876 and September 1877, and had been sent specially by Hopkins's company to put together the high girders.

As a rule Newcombe saw that the riveting throughout the high girders was complete. The rivets fastened the diagonal bars on the bridge, and he went over these rivets as well as over the rivets on the girders with the same care. To Newcombe's mind, the rivets were all good, and he did not think any of them had given way. That could only have happened if the rivet had been left too hot and had contracted, which would have caused it to fly off at the head. If that had happened it would have been detected by the sound of the hammer on checking. However, he emphasised that none of the rivets that held the diagonal bars could possibly have come away so as to let the diagonal bars fall. In Newcombe's inspection of these rivets, they were just as good and as efficient in their workmanship as any of the others.

After the line had opened and he was inspecting its operation, Newcombe sometimes stood upon a pier when a train went past. He felt a motion, a slight jar, something like sitting in a railway carriage, a certain tremor in the bottom, but what it amounted to he could not tell.

When Newcombe climbed up the columns, he did not notice anywhere any problem with the connecting system of the columns, comprising lugs and flanges. These flanges were circular discs with holes for bolts, which fastened one section of column to another, end to end. They were also used to tie the bottoms of the columns to the brick piers. In the angle between column and flange were cast flat triangular brackets, or lugs – projecting wings with bolt holes, designed for the attachment of the tie-bar ends. Newcombe never noticed any lugs that were not tightly attached to the columns, and never saw any separation between the connecting systems where he had been working. However, he would not have seen small cracks in the columns if they had been puttied over. He noticed in the making of the joints that the parts fitted in a very good line, the one with the other. The girders were all made in Middlesbrough and were brought to the bridge in pieces.

Newcombe left the bridge after he had made the connections between the girders; he was finishing the joints during the time ballast trains were running over. As soon as all the joints were effected, his work was done.

Hercules Strachan was a moulder by trade, working at East Foundry, Dundee, and had done that work for about 36 years. He worked as the foreman moulder at the Wormit Foundry connected with the Tay Bridge for about ten months, from July 1874 to April 1875. He was therefore at the foundry before the castings for the bridge were commenced.

A number of the columns for the bridge were cast at the Wormit Foundry during his time. The pig iron was Cleveland iron, together with about 120 tons of scrap iron. This was the first time that Strachan had worked with Cleveland iron, which was not used unmixed, but was mixed with scrap at Wormit. He said that he superintended the casting to the best of his ability, and took pains to see that bad work was not turned out; as a result there was very little bad work while he was there. During his time on the job he only broke up two columns that had come out of the moulds.

Strachan was, however, very much troubled with 'scabs', protuberances left on the iron casting formed by the washing away of the mould wall during the foundry work. However, these were small things, the size of penny pieces (approximately 3.1cm in diameter), half-crowns (approximately 3.2cm in diameter) and 5-shilling pieces (crowns, approximately 3.7cm in diameter). Strachan did not consider that these were serious scabs, and they did not, in his estimation, affect the strength of the column at all. He was also troubled by blow-holes of the type that occurred in ordinary castings, from a pinhead to half a pea in size, but again did not think that they weakened the columns at all.

While he was at the bridge he welded two 'snugs' onto columns; a snug was a projection attached to a column to prevent rotation. One had been a defective snug and the other was one that the dresser had broken during casting

Strachan never saw any cracked columns when he was working – had he done so, he would most decidedly have broken them up. He would have done the same if he had seen any with such big blow-holes as to endanger the column.

Andrew Foreman was also a moulder at Wormit Foundry, starting there shortly after it commenced work for the Tay Bridge and working there for about two years. When he started he was a 'dresser', dressing the columns, which consisted of removing the moulding sand and what were called 'fins', rough places on the castings, preparatory to their going into the lathe to be turned. After that he went to the cupola, which was the furnace in which the iron was melted for the purpose of casting.

In the course of dressing Foreman very frequently came across columns that were 'scabbed'. He chiselled off these excrescences, then, if there was any hole made, he filled it with cement or putty. This had to be done so frequently that a cement – known as Roman cement – was supplied for the express purpose of doing so. Foreman's foreman at the time was Hercules Strachan, who knew that cement was being used.

Foreman put manufactured iron into the cupola with combustible material so as to reduce it to a molten state. As far as he knew he melted Middlesbrough iron or Cleveland pig-iron, which he thought was very bad-quality iron, in that after it was melted there was a terrible lot of refuse in the top of the ladle. Foreman had unsuccessfully tried to melt it and use it again, but it was full of refuse, in his view. This 'rubbish', as Foreman called it, was all through the iron and could not be separated from it.

Foreman had previously seen Scottish iron melted, and the metal he melted in the cupola differed greatly from good Scottish metal with reference to the scum. In good Scottish metal the scum would rise to the surface and, when ladled away, would leave the metal clear and lively. With the iron used at the Wormit Foundry, the scum never got clear away, and remained always sluggish.

Foreman recalled being spoken to about some scrap base-plates, which were lying nearly opposite the cupola. He considered that these were made of good iron, but could not say whether it was Scottish or not, because one could not determine that very easily after it was in scrap form. There were some tons of this iron, and James McGowan, a moulder at Wormit Foundry, ordered Foreman to mix a lot of this scrap with the English 'pigs' to improve it. Foreman did this with about 10 or 12 hundredweight, which he considered improved the quality of the iron.

However, Foreman was stopped by Frank Beattie from carrying out McGowan's instructions with all the iron. Beattie was manager of the department at that time, and said he would bring iron from Middlesbrough, which would sell better after the bridge was finished. Foreman accordingly did not melt any more of the scrap, but left it there, and it was still there when he left, having lain there, without being put to any use, for six or seven months during the two years Foreman was on the site.

Foreman used coke in the cupola, which he also considered of inferior quality, being more charged with sulphur than the coke he had used in other cupolas. This he judged from the fumes and smell that it gave off.

The moulders used Tay water during their work, this being kept in a large tank with appliances for pumping it from the river. The tank and pumping apparatus were part of the original construction of the foundry. This Tay water was salt water at Wormit, and at high water Foreman judged it to be very pregnant with salt, not distinguishable from sea water.

Foreman worked at the foundry for about 18 months under Hercules Strachan, and less under Fergus Ferguson. He worked at the cupola during Ferguson's time, doing nothing else, and Ferguson was his gaffer. At that time there was plenty of scrap iron lying about. Foreman had heard that the plan of the bridge had been changed, and he found there the caissons that had been intended to line the pillars, which had been broken up into scrap iron.

At no time did Ferguson ever instruct Foreman to put any proportion of scrap iron into the pig, but during the time that Foreman was working at the cupola he regularly put in a proportion of that scrap with the pig, generally about one-third. This he did on his own initiative, and did so regularly for two years, except for a period during Strachan's time when there was no scrap to be used up.

Foreman ran out of scrap iron for a time, having used up all that was available, then, after Ferguson came, the scrap came from the jetty. After the orders were given by Frank Beattie to drop it, Ferguson broke up that scrap and Foreman began to melt it again. When McGowan came he wanted to introduce scrap with the 'pig', but he was stopped by Beattie. Except for the time when Foreman was proposing to use it, when Beattie stopped him using it, he used very little scrap in Strachan's time; however, he used scrap during the whole of Ferguson's time.

The columns made during Strachan's time were commenced with the centre portion, and during that time Foreman was putting the small rather than the large columns into place – these were the ones left standing after the bridge went down. Thus all those that were cast in Strachan's time survived, while those cast during Ferguson's time, using one-third scrap, were erected below the high girders that went down. Foreman recalled having broken up defective castings during Ferguson's time, by Ferguson's orders.

Generally, it was Ferguson's custom, whenever any casting came out defective, to direct it to be broken up. Foreman accordingly did this and put it through the furnace again. However, Foreman had seen blistered columns filled up with cement rather than scrapped by Ferguson, and had seen cement put into the centres of the columns. Foreman had not done this under his gaffer Ferguson, but he had done so under Strachan, when he was acting as dresser.

Foreman stated that when he had mixed the iron with scrap, it was not as full of scum. However, even at its best, it was nothing like equal to good Scottish metal. During Strachan's time Foreman generally had broken base-plates rather than broken columns to use as scrap, but he doubted whether they were Scottish iron. Foreman had mixed a deal of such scrap with Cleveland iron during Strachan's time, to go into the new castings, and this was done as often as he had broken columns that he was told to use as scrap. He said he could not describe the metal scrap from those columns at its best as lively.

Foreman said that he did not know why Beattie had ordered him to refrain from mixing in the scrap base-plates lying at the cupola or the scrap lying at the jetty. The base-plates were used while McGowan was in charge, between Strachan and Ferguson, and he used them until he was stopped from doing so. From Ferguson's time scrap was no longer used, and there was no other supply of scrap iron brought to the foundry from any other place except the jetty.

A number of other engineers worked on the bridge. Henry Abel Noble, an engineer inspector, was continually on the bridge inspecting the brickwork, the stonework and the cement work. In addition to these men, Allan Stewart carried out an inspection once a week or thereabouts. He was Bouch's engineering assistant and was an iron founder in his own right and Provost of Renfrew. He had done much work on the sewerage system in Edinburgh, while on the railway front he had done some civil engineering work for the Highland Railway in 1866 and for the North British in 1877. Stewart often inspected the progress of the work at the bridge with Bouch.

When Edgar Gilkes took on the contract, he also took on the staff already working on the job to form his own team. He found them to be a very efficient set of men. They were spoken of very highly by Bouch, who had known them for two years or more, so Gilkes took them exactly as they were, making his own arrangements with them. He had no reason whatsoever to doubt from his subsequent experience the statements made to him by Bouch as to their experience and skill – he always found them both experienced and skilful.

The head of the work was Albert Gröthe, whose account of the design and construction of the Tay Bridge was published in Dundee in 1878. Under him, as head of the foundry, was Frank Beattie, whose duty also extended to any fitting work that had to be done on shore. Frederick Reeves had charge of the general construction on the water, while Gerrit Willem Camphuis had the construction of the underwater part, the foundation. A Mr Jones had charge of the construction of the north end, and the small piers at that end were entirely under his care. The two Delpratt brothers, under General Delpratt, had charge of the putting on of the superstructure. Finally, a Mr Lawrence had charge of the fleet, as it was called. The fitful character of the River Tay made it necessary to have one man who would be responsible for the whole of the craft, because it sometimes proved necessary to bring boats in two or three times a day to keep clear of storms.

George McBeath was employed by Bouch to carry out a careful inspection, and his period of responsibility was from the end of October 1877 until 1878. McBeath's work was such that Gilkes took a close personal interest in it, so far as he could, consistent with the necessities of other work.

Gilkes went to the site of the Tay Bridge fairly frequently, according to necessity. He could not recall how frequently he visited; sometimes it was every fortnight, sometimes not for six weeks, according to how the work was proceeding. When he visited he simply went for two or three days, according to the needs of the work going on.

On taking the contract, Gilkes had also had to take on a certain amount of plant that had belonged to de Bergue, which was part of the arrangement with the North British Railway Company. Part of that plant was the unfinished foundry at Wormit, which Gilkes completed as soon as he could because he thought it was a judicious outlay of money, in order to have the means of doing the work on the spot, even though he would have preferred to have made all the castings at Middlesbrough. Sometimes the upper columns of the bridge varied in length, so Gilkes's men were not able to sink the foundations as low as he had expected; it therefore became convenient to have a foundry on the spot.

When Gilkes was at the bridge he always went through the work that had been done since his previous visit regarding construction, erection and especially foundry work. This he did personally – he did not leave it to the mere report of people under him.

At Wormit he gave no directions with regard to the character of material or the workmanship that was to be used on the bridge. In regard to materials, Gilkes selected them himself at Middlesbrough and sent them to Wormit. He directed that nothing that was not perfect, as far as they could make it by inspection and care, should be passed into the bridge, and he emphasised this himself by repeatedly breaking up castings whose quality he doubted. These included any he found to contain anything like a blow-hole, which would be followed out by a hammer to discover its depth. If the depth might have been injurious to the column, the casting would be broken up. Gilkes thought he had had some 20 columns broken up in his various visits. Beattie had stated that about 15 per cent of the castings were broken up for one fault or another, and Gilkes did not think this an exaggerated figure.

All the raw material was selected and sent from Middlesbrough, with the exception of some scrap from Scotland. All the girders were made at Middlesbrough and sent to Wormit to be put together there before erection. The cast-iron cylinders that were used for the foundations were also made there, and many of the columns, such as the 12-inch raking columns.

The 18-inch and 15-inch columns were made at the Wormit Foundry, but the tie-bars, the iron links that bound together the separate parts of the structure, and the channel-irons were all made at Middlesbrough. Different foremen had responsibility in the different parts of the works at Middlesbrough, and Gilkes himself took the same interest in all the work as his men did. He was there more or less continually, and always in the works, always inspecting the work; indeed, he thought the work of such importance that he daily inspected the construction of the tie-bars and all the work done at Middlesbrough.

Gilkes was asked to consider the question of the sufficiency of the bolts for their task at the bridge. Those made at Middlesbrough by Gilkes's men, which were a large proportion of the total, were inspected, as all his work was inspected. Those that were bought, notably those from the Cleveland Nut & Bolt Company, were inspected in Gilkes's store-house as soon as they were brought in. Henry Law, the engineer who carried out inspection work on behalf of the Court of Inquiry, confirmed that the bolts were perfectly satisfactory. Every bolt was examined by Gilkes's men, and many were taken to the anvil to test the quality of the iron.

The Cleveland Nut & Bolt Works, close to Gilkes's works, made a very considerable number of the bolts. Gilkes's made 11,000 1⅛-inch bolts, but did not make more because the bolt-making arrangements were so occupied that it was more convenient to get them made by Cleveland Nut & Bolt Works. It was really like making them themselves, as Gilkes's men were in there constantly. Gilkes had the bolts brought to his own yard and tested there, then returned to the Cleveland Works. Gilkes never heard any suggestion that these bolts were made of bad iron or that they were not sufficient and proper for the purpose.

The holes at the ends of the tie-bars were cast at Middlesbrough, and the bars were fitted together with a slotting-machine. The cotters were also made by Gilkes at Middlesbrough, as were the gibs; the gibs and cotters were two-part contrivances with fixed and moveable wedges used to fasten connecting rods together. The drawings of these various parts were from time to time furnished by the engineer to Gilkes and were executed at his behest.

Gilkes's practice was to test the cast iron from which the castings were to be made, but he did not test the wrought iron unless called upon by the engineer to do so. Gilkes reiterated that he himself was constantly overseeing the work at the Wormit Foundry, where he saw with his own eyes how the casting was being done. All the columns were cast at Wormit in the ordinary way, with a top and bottom box or flask.

There had been complaints, the Court of Inquiry was told, about the quality of metal used. However, Gilkes, during the whole process of the works, had had nothing of the kind suggested to him by anybody. He was sure that poor-quality metal did not exist except in the ignorance of the men who gave such evidence – they did not know the nature of the iron they were speaking of. They did not know how to manage it and they had not had the management of it. Gilkes firmly believed that, in point of fact, such defects did not exist in the iron, and said again that no complaint of any kind had been made of such a thing in the whole course of the work.

Gilkes clearly had a great deal to do with the casting, and explained some of the methodology to the Court of Inquiry. Vertical (as opposed to horizontal) casting was adopted so that the core could be kept true in the exact centre of the pipe or column that was being made. However, Gilkes would have preferred to have cast the columns horizontally, and believed that they would have been generally better if cast in that way.

Frederick Reeves was an assistant engineer employed by the contractors for the Tay Bridge works. At the time he gave evidence to the Commissioners he was working for the Royal Railway Company in Portugal, and had left his home in Lisbon to attend the Court of Inquiry at the request of the North British Railway Company. He had been first engaged on the Tay Bridge contract under the employment of Messrs de Bergue & Co, and remained there after the contract was taken over by Messrs Hopkins, Gilkes & Co. Reeves left the bridge officially on 28 December 1877.

Reeves was a civil engineer, and was in charge of the works after Albert Gröthe left them, before the completion of the work, and the men were under his orders. Reeves's personal attention was more devoted to the lower part of the work – the foundations, the floating of the caissons and the floating of the girders and other matters. He had nothing whatever to do with the erection of the high piers, although he did see them erected; he used to be frequently about in order to give directions, but not to inspect the work – several other people were involved in that. Most of the work in the high girders was put together under the inspection of William Delpratt.

Reeves also had nothing to do with the Wormit Foundry – his responsibility lay with the construction of the bridge, not the manufacture of its components. Therefore he was not responsible for inspecting the columns when they went from the foundry to the bridge – his task was simply to erect them.

Reeves was asked if Bouch's assistants were regular and careful in their inspection of the work as it proceeded. He replied that it was difficult for him to answer that question, because the work was 2 miles in length and very often Reeves was engaged for some hours in one spot; therefore Bouch's assistants might be very busy a mile and a half off for all he could tell. Latterly, George McBeath had particularly to supervise the work Reeves was doing, having been appointed inspector with a view of going over all the bridge. Reeves thought McBeath was rather meticulous in some particulars, and if he erred, he erred on the side of over-carefulness and over-strictness.

Reeves was asked about the holding-down bolts, the bolts that came up through the stonework and went into the base-pieces of the columns. They were put through the two upper courses of stone in the large piers, and there were four of those bolts to each base. These bolts should have all been exactly at the same level, and Reeves always endeavoured that this should be the case, but in one or two cases there was a slight difference in level, which was not observed at the time they were cemented.

Latterly, on some of the piers the base-plates were put on the bolts before the latter were cemented, but Reeves had used templates for adjusting the bolts in the usual way. On average they were cemented after at least a month or six weeks. Reeves recalled two instances of bolts that stood up particularly high when the cementing had been finished, and it was necessary at times to put in extra washers in consequence of a bolt rising up

During the last two months that Reeves was at the bridge, he was in charge of the works. Albert Gröthe had left early in the month of November, and Gilkes had requested Reeves to stay on to see that every detail of the bridge was finished from top to bottom, asking him to assume the duty of going through the details to see that they were in order.

When McBeath went over the piers, he discovered a few things that required, as he considered, to be altered. There was something to do on nearly all the piers. For instance, in some cases the bolts fastening the flanges and columns together had two washers instead of one. Also, one or two of the horizontal tie-bars were not screwed tight and in some cases one or two had to be removed and more thread put on the bolt in order to screw up the nut. The gibs and cotters were also all gone over.

Six or eight, or in some cases ten, men were put on each pier, and they had to continue working at that pier until McBeath had gone over it carefully and stated that the work was completely finished. Examination would be undertaken by the stroke of a hammer. The method of testing was that a man would strike the cotter, and if it did not give it was passed, but if it was loose it would have to be driven further in.

During his final two months Reeves went over, or saw gone over, all the piers in the high part of the bridge. It was his firm belief that there was not a single cotter loose. They had all been put in at the same time. The contractor was to have finished work on the bridge before Reeves left, and it would be part of Reeves's duty under McBeath's inspection to see that the cotters were put in if any were absent. During Reeves's last two months at the bridge there were ballast trains crossing it, perhaps four or five times a day. He had himself heard the 'chattering' referred to by other witnesses, before the bars were perfectly tightened.

In Reeves's view, this chattering was caused when any of the tie-bars, formed by two flat bars of iron crossing diagonally, were naturally a little out of line before they crossed each other; if they were loose, and if there was any vibration, one bar would strike against the other. Consequently there was a noise, a chattering, of one piece of iron hitting against the other. However, he never heard any of these bars vibrating after they had been properly tightened. Reeves had also been down in different parts of the piers when trains had been passing, and his attention was particularly drawn to the noise because he had heard the tie-bars chattering on a previous occasion. The Commission then turned to the manufacture of the tie-bars, most of which, Reeves said, had been made in Middlesbrough. Reeves had often seen those that came from Middlesbrough at the works, and they appeared to have been well-made.

It was part of Reeves's duty before leaving the bridge to examine whether all bolts had been put in – it was his duty to examine everything. However, he did not go outside the girders to examine every bolt. He had been outside four or five L-girders with McBeath, and one or two of the bolts that he had objected to had been taken out and replaced by others. McBeath called Reeves's attention to instances in which some of the bolts, in his judgement, were not satisfactory. To the best of his belief there were no 18-inch columns with only four bolts instead of eight when he left.

Reeves had inspected all the channel-irons, and was satisfied that they had been properly screwed up. However, he did not see the erection of all the columns in the high girders. He saw a large number of column sections go out from the jetty, because he used to order them to be sent out as they were required. He did not have to inspect the work until each column section was put upon the one below it. The bolt-holes in the 18-inch columns were all cast at Middlesbrough (Reeves had not therefore seen them made), and the corresponding holes in the L-girders were punched off there too.

Reeves's examination with McBeath was on behalf of the railway company's engineer before the work was taken out of the hands of the contractors. As far as Reeves was concerned, he made the examination carefully. He could not, himself, examine every place to see whether or not the tie-bars were correctly fastened, but the men Reeves had working there got their instructions from him and not from the inspector; and where the inspector saw that anything was wrong that had been passed and overlooked by the men, he would report it to Reeves, who would see that it was put right.

There were a number of men at each pier who were under Reeves's orders to do for McBeath anything that the latter required. If anything was done by them not quite correctly or if anything was left undone that McBeath had desired, that particular matter was brought to Reeves's notice.

When Reeves left the bridge he had not seen whether the ties that came from Middlesbrough had been properly punched – he did not see if they were punched or slotted with a slotting-machine. However, he was satisfied that they were properly cut, as he had inspected them several times. Reeves was asked if he drew a distinction between the metalwork that came from Middlesbrough and the rest. He replied that there were a few of the sling-bars that were made at the local works, and he thought that these were properly punched; however, he also thought they were not quite as well finished as those from Middlesbrough, as there was no slotting-machine at the local works.

When Reeves left the bridge at the end of December 1877 he was not aware of any remaining 'chattering' of the tie-bars, and all the bolts were tight. However, the large number of packing pieces used after Reeves left showed that a considerable loosening must have taken place thereafter. If any piers had moved over at the top, it would have brought strains to bear on all the ties that were in the line of that force. Reeves decidedly thought that there must have been a horizontal movement of the columns.

The Court of Inquiry's evidence revealed some sloppiness in the bridge's construction. The columns had many holes in their castings, which a witness admitted to simply filling up to disguise them. This evidence came from John Gibb, a dresser employed at the Wormit Foundry. He had been employed there for about two and a half years, and it was his job to dress any columns that had holes in them. Gibb found a few such columns, with holes about a quarter of an inch to an inch or so deep, although they did vary in size. The largest hole he found had been about 3 inches in diameter and three-eighths of an inch deep. All these columns had been passed at the Wormit Foundry and sent to the bridge for use.

All these holes Gibb filled up with 'Beaumont egg' (or 'beaumontage'), a mixture of iron filings and cement. Sometimes he filled up blow-holes in a lug, the biggest of which he filled being about 3 inches in depth. Other holes he found he filled up by pouring in molten lead; the largest hole he had filled up with lead had been about three-eighths of an inch deep. Gibb had done this two or three times all the time he was there, and some other men working for the company saw it done.

Gibb saw cracks between a 'snug' and a flange from time to time, where there had been bits burned on. The men put cloths or sacks over these cracks to hide them. Gibb thought he was hiding them from the contractors. They were immediately painted, which hid them even more. The largest such crack he dealt with in that way was about 3 or 4 inches in length. None of the cracks were filled up with Beaumont egg. Gibb received orders to fill up these cracks from his boss, Fergus Ferguson. The aim, Gibb said, was to hide the holes from Mr Gröthe, or Mr Gilkes, or Mr Beattie.

Gibb saw columns broken up with a big hammer when they were bad, which was done on Ferguson's orders; some were twisted, and some had big blow-holes. Some of them were filled up and others broken.

Gibb had nothing to do with the turning, so he did not know what became of the columns after they left him, although he did paint them after they left the turners' hands. However, after the holes had been filled up he finished the repairs with putty. David Hutton then put the columns onto the barges for transport to the construction site, where they were used on the bridge. They were not broken up.

Gibb's evidence of malpractice at Wormit Foundry was backed up by moulder David Hutton. He had worked at the site for between two and three years and was engaged in casting the columns for the bridge.

Hutton thought that the casting was done with very bad iron. Like Foreman, this he judged from the bad scum upon it, which he never managed to get rid of entirely. The columns Hutton helped to cast had flanges at both ends, and lugs for the tie-rods. These lugs were supposed to come out of the mould on the column, but Hutton had sometimes taken columns out of the mould without the lugs cast on, so new ones had to be burned on. Such burned-on lugs should have been as strong as the original casting but generally they were cracked at the side.

Every column Hutton saw with a lug burned on was cracked. He could not say how often this occurred as it was so frequent. Sometimes the lugs on the columns got knocked off accidentally and new lugs were burned on in the same way. In these cases Hutton saw a crack between the lug and the flange. The burning-on was done very carefully, although it could not be made as close as the original casting; if they made it as secure as the cast lug itself, the column was generally cracked, caused by the hot iron on the cold body of the column, even when the column was heated before the new metal was poured in. However, they were not heated to anything like the temperature of the metal Hutton was pouring on – he thought the column could have been made hotter than it was. The hotter it was made, the more likely the new metal was to adhere, and the less likely the column was to crack.

These columns came out of the shop and were sent to the bridge for use. Columns were also very frequently 'scabbed', and the scabs were chipped off with a hammer and chisel. This process did not leave a weakening hole in the column, but in Hutton's view was bound to reduce its strength for resisting pressure.

Hutton confirmed that any holes found in the columns were filled up with cement, and there were piles of cement and putty there for that purpose, then the repairs were painted over. This was done very frequently. The foreman knew it was going on – indeed, everybody in the shop knew it was being done.

A detailed although unplanned examination of the bridge was conducted by the men who painted it. They worked on every part of the girders, and were therefore asked by the Court of Inquiry about matters such as any loose rivets they found on the structure and the quality of the workmanship. Their painting obviously took place immediately after the completion of erection work of the bridge and before it opened for rail traffic.

One such painter was David Dale, a seaman who lived in Dundee. He spent some three months working at the Tay Bridge, the whole period (bar nine days) while the bridge was being painted. Dale assisted in painting the high girders and the girders at each side, north and south. In the course of his work he noticed that the whole structure was fastened together with rivets and bolts. When he came in with the painters he saw a lot of bolts lying about on the top of the bridge, although not on the girders themselves; these had evidently not been needed. Dale had painted one side of a lower boom on the east side, and there was another man clearing it out; there was a lot of gravel and stuff in the boom together with the bolts. Some bolts were thrown down with the gravel and others were gathered up and put on the top of the bridge – it was just rubbish that had been left in when the rivets were put in.

Dale saw that nothing had fallen out of the bridge, because everything was in its place. Fallen bolts and nuts from the structure would not have been found on any part of the bridge, because the top of the bridge overlapped the lower boom. Dale did not see any part of the girders with any hole that ought to have had a bolt in it.

A great many trains passed each way on each day Dale was engaged there; these were ballast trains connected with the laying of the track, the last stage of the bridge's engineering before it was painted. Trains coming onto the bridge created motion, he felt, a sort of shaking motion from side to side, but never up and down. It sort of trembled, he said. It was more perceptible inside the high girders than it was on the open girders north and south. It was such a strong movement that Dale had to hold on to his paint pot or secure it in some way, depending on where it was. The pot was most secure when set on top of the bridge where the rails were laid. When he was working on the top of the high girders, when his paint pot was nearly empty, he had seen it shift 3 inches with the shaking, although it did not move when it was full or half full. He noticed that some parts of the bridge swayed more from the motion of the train than others, and felt it most in the northernmost large girders.

Dale observed that the train that was going the fastest caused the most movement in the bridge, and the movement increased as the speed increased. He felt the movement as soon as a train entered upon the bridge on the south side and passed over the brick piers. It began to shake gradually until the train got alongside him, then the effect faded. When Dale was in the high girders, he felt the vibration of the bridge or the movement most as a train came north of the brick piers.

Peter Donegany, a 19-year-old apprentice painter, spent two months on the Tay Bridge working from the north side towards the south end of the large girders, inside all the high girders. In the course of this painting, he noticed a good many bolts or screws or bolt-heads lying about, which had to be removed to allow him to paint. He also noticed a few empty bolt-heads in the lower booms of the lower girders, in the part of the bridge that went down in the disaster. Donegany noticed a few bolt-holes elsewhere on the bridge, on the small girders, the ones nearest the shore to the north of the high girders, but at that point he did not notice any bolts lying around as if they had come out. The empty holes were not in a line, but randomly scattered about.

Donegany noticed that a passing train would cause an up and down motion in the bridge, which he could feel when he was standing on the bridge, and also when he was on the scaffolding. This motion was on the booms of the bridge and on its structure, and on the large girders it was more violent. He felt the same motion at every part of the bridge whenever a train crossed, on both the small and the large girders, but more distinctly inside the high girders than outside them. He felt the motion before a train came up to where he was working, and it was enough to upset his paint pots unless he had secured them, which he consequently did.

When a train was coming on to the large girders at the south end and he was at the north end, he felt the bridge shake before it entered the high girders – it went back and forth, east and west. Donegany thought that the strongest motion when a train was passing him was up and down rather than side to side, which happened every time a train went past.

The holes that Donegany saw were meant for rivets, being in line with other rivets. He was unsure how many he had seen in the lower boom. He had also seen holes in the high girders, where no water would go through; they were therefore holes intended for rivets. They were not at regular distances from each other. Donegany saw two or three of those holes in the high girders, no more. In the lower girders he saw about six altogether, underneath the bridge, where the lower girders were.

John Evans was a mill-overseer and lived in Dundee. He was also present at the painting of the Tay Bridge during the whole job, and during that time he too occasionally came across empty bolt-holes, generally in the angle-irons outside the boom. They were not holes left to let water run through off the bridge – those were in the centre of the boom, and he had seen such holes during his work. The holes he had seen were bolt-holes with the rivets missed out. Evans had no idea how many such holes he saw during his time on the bridge, but he never found more than one rivet hole empty at any place, just occasional empty holes with rivets on either side of them still in place. Evans found a bolt occasionally here and there where a rivet ought to have been.

Evans found those empty bolt-holes in the bottom of the bridge to the north of the large girders, where he also found rivets without their heads. A great many heads were off, and his impression was that they had been 'sprung'. He could tell by looking at the rivet-hole whether anything that had been there originally was not there then. Some of the bars were hanging off altogether, hanging down and completely displaced, in consequence of the want of rivet-heads. He saw at least two of the diagonal bars hanging off in that way; these bars were intended to support the vertical columns, but now they were off.

In the lower boom of the girders Evans saw a good many bolts and rivets lying loose. He thought they had been laid there during the construction of the bridge, but did not for a moment think that they were bolts and screws that had been sprung out of their place.

Evans was engaged continuously from the north cabin to No 14 pier south, the southernmost high girder, and went from one end straight to the other on the west side of the big girders. During the four months that he worked on the bridge a great many ballast trains crossed it, having, Evans felt, a great effect upon it. The most pronounced and severe effect was the oscillation, the side-to-side movement, but Evans also felt a vertical movement. Like Dale, he remarked that trains crossed the bridge at different speeds, the fastest ones making the bridge move most. He felt the lateral movement most when he was up on the scaffolding. A long time before a train passed him the bridge began to shake from side to side, and continued to do so until it had passed him.

Evans first perceived the vertical movement perhaps four or five girders distant, and it was so distinct that the bridge commenced to lift him. He could feel this vertical motion when he was standing on the deck of the bridge – there was no mistaking the fact that the bridge was going up and down from the effect of the passing train. It was a very violent motion, and kept time with the movement of the crank of the locomotive. It affected things he had placed on the bridge: he had seen the spilling of a pail of water a long while before a train approached. He thought he could feel the oscillation half a mile off.

Evans therefore always secured his paint pots with every passing train, otherwise he thought they would have gone to the bottom. How he made them fast would depend on the job he was on. Sometimes he secured them by a lanyard made of three-ply spun yarn, but this did not work – it parted, and he lost his paint pot. Evans attributed the parting of the lanyard to the vibration of the train passing.

Evans knew that the men working for the North British Railway's inspector of the permanent way, Henry Noble, were on the bridge putting right anything that was wrong by the use of rivets. However, Evans and his colleagues were only speaking to each other, and were not reporting to headquarters; Evans therefore did not tell anybody about the rivet-heads being off. He had nothing to do with it – he had had no instructions to mention anything that he found wrong. He acknowledged that the rivet-heads being off was an important thing, but he and the other painters had not got an overseer over them. He thought it was the duty of a man, if he found anything wrong, to tell his own superior or the men there to put things right, but not in this case because the gaffer was there, Edward

Simpson, the company's diver, who superintended the painters. However, Evans did not tell Simpson anything about what he had found, that a great number of rivet-heads were off, a few dozen. The men working would have found it easy to see that they were off – no man accustomed to that kind of work going along to look at the state of the bridge could have missed seeing them. Evans found rivet-heads lying below where he saw the breaks, and anybody else going along would have seen the broken rivet-heads, which were amongst the ballast. He acknowledged that it would have been better if he had told his superiors about these things, but he did not at the time because the men were not instructed to do anything of the sort. Both he and his colleagues thought it was better to hold their tongues.

Evans found loose diagonal bars over every one of the piers, and found them all loose in No 10 pier. Occasionally they were loose in other piers. Not one pier was fast – the bars all shook in his hand going up, all slack in rivet. However, while they were all slackened, none had given way – they were all still on.

David Pirie was a painter in Dundee, and went over the Tay Bridge to offer to contract to paint all of it. His examination was therefore pretty careful, his primary object being to examine the extent and character of the work for which he proposed to contract, and how to stage the bridge, in particular that part which was above the footway. He made his examination at the end of May 1879, but in the event did not get the contract.

During his examination Pirie saw a good many bolts and screws lying upon the upper portion of the booms, but he presumed they were just what had been left over in the construction of the bridge. He never observed whether any bolt was out of its place, nor did he observe whether any were without any of the screws or heads on them. He spent three different days conducting his examination, and during all that time the bridge was being used by trains; when they were crossing he always noticed the bridge vibrate.

Pirie was always standing only 4 feet or so from the trains when they crossed the bridge, and felt the vibration as soon as they entered the bridge. His principal position was at the north end of the fallen girders, to the south of what was to remain standing, inside the high girders. At that point he could feel the vibration of the bridge when a train came upon it at the south end. This was slight as the train entered the bridge but it gradually increased until it came with a waving vibration while it passed. Pirie felt the motion increase to become this wavy motion before the train came up to him, increasing as the train advanced. As the train passed him, the vibration was very great and he noticed that the latticework vibrated very much. He did not think the vibration was enough to have shaken a paint pot off the bridge, but nevertheless he could see it quite distinctly.

Pirie said that he could both see and hear the vibration of the bridge when a train crossed. At times this vibration was more violent than at others, and he accounted for this by the speed of the trains, both passenger and goods. He thought that they went through the high girders at a great speed, although he was not able to estimate it. The vibration affected the latticework rather than the upper part of the bridge, the booms, and he only observed this vibration within the high girders. When he was outside them as a train approached, he went within the girders to avoid the draught that the crossing train occasioned.

Pirie had certainly not had experience before of being so close to a running train as the 4 feet or so he was away from trains on the Tay Bridge, so it was a novel experience for him. He had also not had much to do with great iron railway bridges. He was therefore not in a position to compare what vibration there was on the Tay Bridge with the vibration on any other similar structure.

Pirie subsequently used the Tay Bridge as a passenger, although not frequently. As a passenger he was never aware of the vibration the trains occasioned on the bridge, in either direction.

Peter Robertson was also a painter who lived in Dundee, from where he carried out painting on the Tay Bridge, working for Mr Bamlett of Sunderland, who had been awarded the contract to paint the bridge. Robertson worked on the bridge for between four and five weeks, on the high girders only, from about the fifth pier on the south side northwards. His job was to paint every bit of the bridge, the latticework, the high girders and the booms, from the underneath to the top. There were about 30 hands doing the painting.

Robertson found a good many loose screws, screw-nuts and bolts lying around, some 2 or 3 hundredweight of them; they were lying inside the lower booms, all along each side. There was a man on each side of the bridge clearing up each boom before Robertson began painting, clearing away these bolts and any other rubbish that was there – sand and pebbles and other items that had fallen off the bridge into the boom.

Robertson observed that the plates of the booms were riveted, and overlapped each other. However, the nuts and bolts that he saw lying along the boom were similar in character to those that had been used in fixing the plates. None of the bolts were out of their holes and no bolt-holes were empty.

A great many trains passed each day while he was at the work, both north and south. Robertson felt the bridge shake very much whenever a train crossed, both when he was on the bridge itself and on the scaffolding that had been put in the bridge. The shaking was about equal in the two locations. When he was on the bridge and it made him go up and down, he naturally supposed that whatever he was standing on was going up and down. The motion was very violent, sometimes more so than others. Robertson felt the bridge go up and down, but not from side to side, and it happened every time a train crossed, whatever type it was. He was unsure which made the bridge vibrate more, a heavy goods train or a faster passenger train. He knew that, with the passenger trains, the higher the speed, the greater the motion. Robertson noticed that some trains travelled at higher speeds than others, a good deal higher.

Robertson could not leave anything standing without its being fixed for fear of it being vibrated off the bridge. His paint pots and other things were always fastened on to or inside the boom, where they could not have been shaken off. When he was actually painting, if he had not fixed his material in some way to prevent it being thrown off, that violent up and down motion would have done so, especially on the scaffolding.

Robertson did some of his work standing on the deck of the bridge, and there he also felt the bridge vibrate when a train went past. The painters became more accustomed to it by and by, and did not take so much notice of it latterly.

Returning to the matter of the loose bolts, it was not evident to Robertson whether they had been used for joining the bridge sections together, and had been left there. He did not know what they were for. He also never noticed any screw or bolt loose. It was quite evident to him that these had been used when they were making the bridge and were there to be taken away. They had obviously been left there for some reason. Robertson was sure they had not fallen off the bridge – they were simply to be taken away with other rubbish that had accumulated in the course of the work.

An account of the engineering of the bridge was then given to the Court of Inquiry by George McBeath, who had inspected the ironwork of the structure on behalf of Bouch after its completion. He had been working for 18 years as a journeyman boilermaker and was an inspector working for the Montrose & Arbroath Railway. He spent the period from 7 July 1877 to May 1878 on his inspection work, and left just before the painting began.

As an inspector, it was his duty to oversee the work and see that it had been satisfactorily done by the contractors. When he came to the bridge, 12 of the large girders had been erected, and one remained to be erected. McBeath paid particular attention to the high girders, because he could get at them relatively easily.

McBeath generally tested them by tapping them with his hand and with a hammer. That way he could tell whether a rivet was loose or tight. He found many that were loose, and these he had taken out and replaced with tight ones. This was something he had always found to be necessary whenever he had inspected riveting, and it was not noteworthy at the Tay Bridge. After he had gone over the rivets and rejected the loose ones, the riveting was tight and well done.

There were some rivet holes without any rivets in them in the high girders, but McBeath did not think that any rivet being removed could possibly affect the stability of the bridge. There were no rivet holes in the lower booms, although there were some holes left for letting water out. Additionally, there were a good many of the rivet-heads that McBeath had directed to be cut lying about the bridge.

McBeath inspected the columns of the bridge by starting at the bottom and climbing up, going round each from the bottom right up to the top. When he got to each stage in his ascent, he walked around the bracing, round the columns and round the piers. At every stage he examined all joints, looking for bad workmanship. He always carried his hammer with him in his pocket, and when he saw anything that was sprung or doubtful, he tested it.

He found that there were some short bolts into the columns that were so short that they did not have a good hold. He had these taken out and replaced with bolts of proper length. When McBeath finished, it was his judgement that the columns were all sound. He found nothing wrong with any of the lugs, except for three pieces broken off; these he had chipped off and malleable iron lugs put on. He thought that something must have come up against them and knocked them off. When he left them they were quite fit to hold the diagonal bracing pieces. There was nothing to suggest the impending disaster.

The adequacy of the lugs was also commented upon by Willem Camphuis, the assistant engineer employed by the contractors for the Tay

Bridge works. One of his tasks was to test the adequacy of the workmanship on the bridge, and in that capacity he inspected the lugs by hammering them. In one instance, which he distinctly remembered, he expressed some doubt to the foreman about the solidity of the 'snug'. Camphuis took up a sledge-hammer and gave it a good swing round, which would have knocked off a perfectly sound lug. But the lug stood it perfectly well.

4

DRIVERS AND GUARDS

*'He was certain he never reached a speed as
high as 40mph on any part of the route.'*

O nce the bridge had been built, painted and opened to traffic, those
experiencing it most were the drivers and guards of the trains on the
Tay Bridge line. The Court of Inquiry took a close interest in the manner in
which trains had been driven on the line, and was particularly interested in
the speed at which trains crossed the bridge, obviously trying to assess
whether excessive speed had contributed to the lost train striking against the
bridge and contributing to its fall. Both drivers and guards of trains were
quizzed on this point. An overview of the question of speed was provided
by William Robertson, the harbour-master of Dundee, who had, as has been
seen, given evidence to the Court of Inquiry as an eye-witness, and was to
do so as a passenger. He had logged the speed of trains for a long time, and
the Court probed him for any evidence of excessive speed by drivers on the
line.

The report of the Court of Inquiry concluded on the question of the speed
of drivers over the Tay Bridge line, notwithstanding the recommendation of
General Hutchinson, Her Majesty's Inspector of Railways, that the speed of
the trains on the bridge should be restricted to 25mph, that the railway
company did not enforce that recommendation, and much higher speeds
were frequently run on portions of the bridge.

After the Tay Bridge was opened, the North British Railway captured 84 per
cent of the traffic from Edinburgh to Dundee, much out-pacing the rival
Caledonian Railway. John Anderson was an NBR passenger engine driver,

and had worked for the company for about 16 years. When the Tay Bridge was opened he worked on the section of the line between St Andrews and Dundee and crossed the bridge at least daily from 1878 until it fell. The first year he crossed the bridge about ten times a day – that was before the Newport route had opened. After the Newport line opened, he crossed the bridge from four to eight times every day, going via Tayport and Newport; before that he had travelled via St Fort. Anderson's usual routine was that he began the day with the morning train, the 8.20am from St Andrews, due at Dundee at 9.10am. His last train was the 4.00pm to St Andrews.

Before the Newport line opened, the speed was restricted to 3mph at the south cabin, and thereafter it was restricted to 2mph. Anderson always observed this restriction on the trains he was driving, due to having to receive or give up the baton or single-line staff at the cabins at either end. This staff, as has already been seen, was given by the signalman to a member of the locomotive crew, and without its possession a train was not allowed onto the single-track bridge. This ensured that there were never two trains on the bridge at the same time. Generally, the time from cabin to cabin was from 5 to 5½ minutes from south to north, which Anderson timed with his watch. From St Andrews he was usually driving a tank engine, which he thought was a 'splendid' engine and would get up to speed very quickly. When it started up smartly, the speed across the whole bridge was pretty even, barring the 500 or 600 yards from the south cabin and the 600 or 700 yards coming to the north cabin.

There was absolutely no material difference in how it felt in going through the high girders from the rest of the line. Anderson's speed through the high girders was usually something below 25mph, and he told the Court of Inquiry that he was certain he never reached a speed as high as 40mph on any part of the route. Indeed, he thought it would have been impossible to get that speed even from such a splendid engine as his. This was, however, contrary to allegations of excessive speed made against drivers, including one against Anderson himself.

In the mornings with the passenger trains he drew nine or ten carriages, with one or two vans. The carriages were always full of passengers at that time, although there were not as many in the afternoon. The morning trains were therefore heavy.

Anderson had crossed the bridge in all kinds of weather, and had never felt the least movement upon the bridge in going over, up and down or side to side. He had been spoken to by James Smith, the Station Master at Dundee, about a complaint that had been made by the former Provost of Dundee, William Robertson. Anderson saw them both on the platform one day, just before starting his train for the south. Smith told Anderson that Provost Robertson had been speaking to him about the speed being too high, but Anderson thought Robertson had been referring to a train other than the one he had been driving. This was the only occasion Anderson ever received comment from the public about his speed. The longest Anderson had ever timed a train going across the bridge, from south to north, had been something near 6 minutes.

In 1879 there was a boat that also crossed the Tay regularly, and if she got away promptly she could be the first into Dundee. But if Anderson's train started from the station when the ferry left the pier, the train would be into Dundee first. Anderson usually got away from Newport on time, although he had sometimes run a minute or two late; sometimes the boat was away from Newport before Anderson's train started.

Anderson reaffirmed that the highest speed at which he ever went across the bridge was 25mph, as his orders stipulated. These orders required the regulation speed to enable a train to go from one station to the other in the advertised time. On those occasions when Anderson was a minute or two late at Newport, he did not try to get into Dundee at his right time: if he was late starting, he was always late in arriving. Anderson was quite sure from actual observation that his trains would never make up any part of a minute lost at Newport by the time they reached the station at Dundee. He knew this from always looking at his watch when he arrived at Dundee.

Station Master Smith only spoke to Anderson on that one occasion, when he had been with the Provost. Smith had said, 'John, ex-Provost Robertson has been complaining to me just now about some trains he came across in some days past, that their speed is about 40mph.' Anderson said nothing to Smith, but smiled to himself: he considered it was perfect nonsense. He had never tried to race the boat – if it got away first, he never tried to get in before it. It made absolutely no difference to how he crossed the bridge.

Anderson had driven across iron bridges before, although not a large span such as the Tay Bridge. He therefore knew from experience on such bridges that he could feel vibration, which was due to the bridge itself, and was different from vibration on the rest of the route. On the Tay Bridge he never felt any vibration or oscillation that was due to the bridge itself.

John Brand had been a passenger engine driver in the employment of the North British Railway Company for 28 years at the time the Tay Bridge went down; his son-in-law, George Ness, died in the disaster. For the most recent 16 months of Brand's service he had been driving on the branch between St Andrews and Dundee, having begun work there three months after the Tay Bridge had opened in 1878. Initially he drove between Burntisland and Dundee, crossing the bridge four times a day, twice north and twice south. When he was put on the St Andrews branch he crossed four times a day one week, and eight times a day the next. When the Newport line was opened, Brand drove trains travelling via Tayport and Newport the whole time, morning, midday and afternoon. He often drove the train that left St Andrews at 6.20am, in turn with John Anderson.

Brand always acted upon the regulation about slowing down at the signal cabins. On going from the south to the north he crossed the bridge at 23 or 24mph from cabin to cabin. He could get a little more speed at the high girders than at each end, but he never exceeded 24mph on the bridge between the high girders. He had never crossed the bridge from south to north in less than 5½ minutes; sometimes it had taken him 7 minutes.

Brand never felt any movement in the bridge, up or down or from side to side – it was very smooth on the whole of the journey. He never had any fear for the bridge's safety, and nobody had ever complained to him about running too quickly. The locomotive foreman, James Moyes, had spoken to him on one occasion, telling him that there had been some complaint about the St Andrews speed 'going hard'. He did not, however, ask Brand at what speed he had been running. He told Brand he should be canny, and not reach too high a speed, for there were complaints. Brand did not time the train often, perhaps once in a day or every two days. In total he thought he might have timed his journeys a hundred times, which he did by standing with his watch in hand, as well as attending to his duties as driver. He did not look at the watch until he came to the cabin.

William Coutts was another passenger engine driver, and had been driving engines for nine years. He had been driving passenger trains via the St Andrews, Leuchars and Tayport route to Dundee since the Tay Bridge opened in May 1878; he did not run between St Andrews and Dundee by the St Fort route. He had continued to drive the route until the bridge fell, driving alternately with Anderson and Brand. Coutts did the journey at first six times a day, three in each direction, and latterly eight times a day, four in each direction.

From the south to the north cabins his journey took 5½ to 6 minutes, and he had often timed this with his watch, finding that it took about the same time for the journey in each direction. His longest journey in either direction had been 6 minutes. From Dundee he took a slightly longer time for the journey, perhaps half a minute more on average. Thus from south to north his train would have been travelling at about 22 or 24mph. This highest speed he would reach normally about the middle of the bridge before he shut off steam, which he usually did at the top of the summit. He slowed down to the specified speed at the cabins to take and deliver the baton. His engine was usually pulling 10 or 11 carriages across the bridge.

Coutts had heard complaints from some people who thought the speed of his trains was too high. Ex-Provost Robertson complained of the speed to William Duncan, a guard, and he in turn spoke to Coutts about it. Duncan asked Coutts if he was running beyond his speed across the bridge, and he replied that he certainly was not. Coutts had been previously in receipt of orders about his speed across the bridge from James Moyes, the locomotive foreman, not to travel at more than 25mph. The Station Master at Newport also spoke to Coutts about his speed on the bridge; he told him that there had been a complaint, and warned him to take care that he did not exceed the regulation speed of 25mph. Coutts was confident that he never reached that speed in his driving across the bridge.

The shortest time Coutts had taken to cross the bridge from cabin to cabin had been exactly 5½ minutes. This he timed by the minute hand of his watch (it did not have a second hand). He was not crossing the bridge with his watch in his hand, looking at it all the time, because he had his duties to attend to; he looked at his watch at the first cabin, and looked at it again at the other, and as far as he could judge the time was 5½ minutes.

His scheduled time from west of Newport to Dundee was 10 minutes, but taking 5½ minutes between the cabins meant that a driver could not do the rest of that journey in 4½ minutes – he was therefore always behind time. If he was behind time leaving Newport, he was the same in Dundee. Sometimes Coutts left West Newport at exactly the proper time, but he never reached Dundee at exactly the proper time, never completing his journey in the advertised time of 10 minutes. The longest time by which he had exceeded his advertised time had been between 2 and 2½ minutes.

Coutts thought that the permanent way on the bridge was in good running order all the way through. It was as good as on the land – if anything, he thought the way was better after a train got onto the bridge, and was not liable to get out of order by a shower of rain or anything of that sort. The track was always maintained to its level and gauge, and he had never felt any danger of his train leaving the rails there. He had also never felt any shock or oscillation when crossing the bridge; he felt no movement at all on the bridge, either up or down or from side to side. He had no doubt that the bridge was safe and sound to the last.

William Duncan was a passenger guard in the North British Railway Company's service, working on trains that ran across the bridge from St Andrews to Dundee. He had begun work on the line at the end of November in the year before the bridge went down, and had been the guard on trains driven by Coutts and James Baxter. About eight or ten times he had taken note of the time the train took in passing from south to north, between the cabins on the bridge; he had timed the journey with his watch, which had been supplied by the NBR for taking times between stations.

The shortest time Duncan thought it had taken a train on which he was the guard to cross the bridge had been 4 minutes and 50 seconds, from north to south; the longest time had been 6 minutes. He only did the journey once in less than 5 minutes, and thought that his average journey time was nearly 6 minutes. All drivers, in his view, kept to the 25mph speed restriction; he had certainly never travelled at a speed of anything like 50mph on any part of the bridge. The highest speed he attained was at about the centre of the high girders.

Duncan took his turn in bringing the first two early trains from St Andrews to Dundee, those that left Newport at 7.00am and 8.35am. The most often he crossed the Tay Bridge in a day was four times, two each way, with Brand and Anderson as his drivers, generally the latter.

Nothing unusual had ever struck Duncan about the speed at which trains crossed the bridge. He considered that the speed restriction of 25mph was never exceeded, and if it had been he would have applied the brake, to keep the train's speed back. Duncan was well aware what a 40mph speed was like, and he had never run at such a speed along any part of the bridge. He had never timed his run from cabin to cabin, although he did time the overall journey.

Duncan thought the speed was highest after trains left the summit, at the centre of the bridge. It was from the centre of the high girders, about four or five spans from the north end, that he looked at the speed of the train. The driver usually shut off steam at the highest part of the bridge, within the high girders, about eight girders from the south end of the high girders and four from the north. When the driver shut off steam, Duncan applied his brake; the guard would usually put on the brake at this point, just as the train was coming out of the high girders.

There was never anything in Duncan's experience of the bridge that suggested to him any doubt concerning its safety or stability. He was well aware of the rule that required that a train should slow down at the cabins at each end to take and give up the baton, and in his experience this rule was carefully observed, trains slowing down to 2mph.

Ex-Provost William Robertson, the harbour-master of Dundee and a regular user of the Tay Bridge line, made a habit of observing from his home the progress of trains over the bridge. He was therefore called by the Court of Inquiry to consider the recurring question of whether trains habitually travelled at too great a speed over the bridge and had thereby contributed to its fall in some way. Robertson was regarded as qualified to comment upon this question both because he made frequent observations of train speeds and because he was an engineer.

Robertson made his observations with a very clear dial watch, with a white face and a good second hand movement. He would take the watch in his hand and the very instant the foremost part of the engine touched the line of the high girders he would fix the second upon his watch, and the instant the front of the engine emerged from the girders he would fix his eyes upon the second hand of the watch. In this way he could be accurate to half a second in his timing. His watch was not a stop-watch, but he believed that, with two fixed points to guide him, a moving watch was equally as good as a stop-watch, although he acknowledged that engineers tended to prefer stop-watches in the hand to set a time.

Robertson saw lights upon the bridge, up on the high girders, on the night of the storm, which were distinctly visible. He saw the train enter the bridge from the south and kept an eye on the bridge after that. His usual view of the bridge from his house meant that he could see trains move from the south shore onto the bridge, then a building interrupted his view for a short distance, after which the bridge was in full view again.

As he looked at the bridge on the night of the 28th he could see very distinctly seven of the piers from the north end that subsequently fell, and could trace them from his window after losing sight of the train behind the building. He kept his eye very steadily on the part of the bridge that was visible beyond the building, but he did not see the train come from behind that building – he saw nothing that he could regard as a train.

Within a couple of minutes he had lost sight of the train leaving the south shore. He had then seen two columns of spray brilliantly illuminated – first one flash, then another. These flashes could have been between what he thought was the summit of the bridge and the north end of it, because he was not straining his eyes looking at it. Robertson thought that the columns of spray were fully a mile away when he saw them, and they were illuminated, either by the lights of the lamps or by something else, so as to be perfectly distinct to his eye – so distinct that there was no mistake whatever that they were columns of spray illuminated by some light or other.

Robertson could not hazard a confident opinion upon whether the light that produced the illumination was the gaslight of the lamps or a flash produced by friction, but his personal conviction and opinion was that the illuminations were produced by the lamps. The conclusion Robertson came to was that the train could not have passed the spot where he saw the columns of spray; he thought that the train had not reached that point when he had seen the spray. At that instant he did not form any view of what the cause of those columns of spray might have been, but immediately afterwards it did occur to him what had caused the flashes of light.

Almost simultaneously with his observing the columns of spray lighting up the bridge it became very dark, and the only inference he could draw from what he had seen was that it was the light upon the bridge turning over that had produced the illumination. This he had seen immediately after that, before the lights were extinguished and the bridge was dark. His opinion was that the bridge had gone over.

The bridge had therefore, in his view, gone over before the train reached the point at which it had given way, that it had given way before the train reached the high girders where he had seen the columns of spray. He did not know definitely that that was the point at which the bridge first gave way; what he believed was that the flash produced by the light at that particular point took place before the train could have reached that point.

Judging from the speed of the train when he saw it, Robertson thought it had certainly entered the high girders, and immediately after the columns of spray had been observed the lights on the bridge had disappeared. Robertson thought the time was between 15 and 20 minutes after 7 o'clock.

Living in Newport, Robertson had been a frequent passenger across the bridge. On various occasions he had observed the speed at which the passenger trains ran across the bridge. He had timed trains from shore to shore, and very often through the high girders. He understood that trains were limited to 25mph on any part of the bridge. Under ordinary circumstances he did not think there was more cause for apprehension of danger arising from the speed of a train within the high girders than on those parts to the north and south of them.

Robertson took close notice of the speed of the train through the girders, and frequent notice of the speed over the whole bridge. The ease with which the train travelled at the two ends of the bridge had produced no uncomfortable feeling in his mind as a passenger, and therefore gave him no concern. The reason why he observed the speed within the girders was that the speed at that particular point did produce some discomfort and concern. He once timed the train at 4 minutes and 20 seconds from signal box to signal box. The length of the bridge from box to box was about 2 miles, so he thought the train was running slightly in excess of 25mph on that section. This speed occasioned very much discomfort in Robertson. He detected that there was a very perceptible vertical vibration, and also a very perceptible lateral vibration upon the bridge with the train running at that kind of speed. When the train was within the girders, it was running at a higher than average speed.

Robertson thought that by the time the train reached the high girders it would be exceeding the speed it had at the south box. Therefore, although the train travelled in excess of 25mph from shore to shore, the actual speed through the high girders was greater than the average.

Robertson had frequently made observations of the exact time occupied in the high girders. On one particular occasion, when the train crossed from cabin to cabin in 4 minutes and 20 seconds, it crossed through the high girders in 60 seconds. The distance from end to end of the high girders was 3,149 feet, so the train was crossing at 35.78 miles per hour. Robertson had often seen trains passing through at a lower speed than that – the longest time he had recorded had been 75 seconds, but more normally the trains that he travelled on crossed in 60 seconds. He had always observed that, when a train was late, it ran faster, and if the train was well up to time it ran slower. Although the trains were usually up to time, he found that trains went through the girders in 60 seconds rather than 75. The fastest Robertson had crossed through the high girders had been at 42.94 miles per hour, and he had experienced such a speed only twice.

Robertson normally travelled north on the railway, returning by boat. On 4 November he took out a season or composition ticket for 12 months. During that month he travelled across the bridge both ways once, and sometimes twice, daily. He finally gave up travelling by the bridge from south to north on about 18 or 20 December, because he did not feel comfortable on the bridge in that direction. He continued to use the bridge in the other direction until the day before it fell. The discomfort he experienced was mental rather than physical, and arose from the high speed of the train. He was anxious for his safety: he considered it dangerous to travel so fast. The same discomfort did not seem to exist to the same extent when he was travelling from north to south; it did not produce anxiety in his mind, and therefore he continued to use the train in that direction.

Robertson had made a complaint to James Smith, the Dundee Station Master, with reference to the speed at which the trains ran through the high girders very shortly after he had taken out his season ticket. He complained to him on three occasions, but Smith's answer was that he was not aware that the trains were travelling faster on the bridge than the time allowed. However, he told Robertson that all the drivers had been particularly warned to keep strictly to time, and that he would himself keep a very strict eye on the trains to see that the time was not exceeded. He received the complaint that Robertson made to him with the greatest civility, and manifested a most anxious desire to have those trains keep the time set down for them.

Robertson did not intimate to Smith at any time that he was about to give up using the trains from south to north before he did so. After his complaint, Robertson noticed that the trains still maintained a speed that he thought dangerous. His complaint seemed to him to have been ignored, so he simply gave up using the railway from south to north. In the middle of November Robertson also spoke to Henry Noble, one of the inspectors of the structure of the bridge, very particularly on the subject of speed. However, he could not make a complaint to him, as he did not think he had any control.

Robertson had observed a train leaving Newport at 7.00am. It was running 10 minutes late and ran at a speed of 12.94mph at the centre of the bridge through the high girders. Robertson had also made particular observations of a train he had travelled in which had left Newport at 7.13am in the middle of December. This train crossed the bridge in 1 minute 20 seconds from cabin to cabin, so its speed on the high part between the girders was 35.78mph.

A regular train – a local to Newport and Dundee – was timed to leave West Newport at 7.13am, but it was often held back until the Aberdeen express on the St Fort line had passed. On the occasions when it was thus delayed, Robertson observed that the average time it took to cross the bridge was 60 seconds, an average speed of 35.78mph, in an effort to try and make up lost time.

Another train was timed to leave Newport at 8.35am, which Robertson always used to come to town by in the morning. This train usually also travelled through the high girders at an average of 35.78mph. As a passenger he had observed that this was the usual speed through the high girders.

When Robertson ceased using the railway from south to north, he instead did the journey by boat, which was equally as convenient for him as the train, although it was not always as quick or as comfortable. Robertson took the less convenient and less comfortable mode of transport simply because he apprehended a risk or danger from using the train going at the speed at which he had observed it to travel.

Returning to the question of the flashes that Robertson had seen, they had appeared to be streams of light and had lasted just a second. They were in a slanting direction from north to south, towards him, probably at an angle of 75 degrees. Robertson had certainly noticed the state of the weather on the night of the 28th, and the storm being so unusual that evening at about 7 o'clock that had led him to be observant that night. There was moonlight, but the moon was shaded by clouds, so he could not detect the bridge but could detect the lights upon it very readily. He saw none of the girders, and the light was not good enough to enable him to see anything that might have fallen from the bridge. The flashes of spray were not bright enough to permit him to see any of the bridge, and the lights he saw before they fell were not enough to light up the bridge.

5
STATION OFFICIALS

'The bridge was not in any way unsafe that night.'

James Moyes was a locomotive foreman of the North British Railway Company and it was his duty to inspect the engines and tenders from time to time to see that they were in proper working order, and to arrange any repairs he found necessary. He inspected the engine and tender of the train from Edinburgh that was to leave St Fort at 7.08pm on Sunday 28 December.

Moyes knew the engine and had prepared it on the Saturday night, when it and the tender had been in good order, and neither needed any repairs. Had they not been so, it would have been in his power to stop the engine going out. He was quite satisfied with them both, so passed them.

William Friend was a ticket collector, also in the service of the North British Railway Company. He worked at St Fort station, about 2 miles south of the Tay Bridge, where he collected the tickets from passengers destined for Dundee by the Tay Bridge route. He remembered on the night of the disaster collecting tickets from the 4.15pm train from Edinburgh, and with him at the station were Robert Morris, the St Fort Station Master, and Alexander Ingles, a porter. Friend confirmed that the marshalling of the train was, after the engine and tender, one 3rd Class coach followed by a 1st Class coach, then two 3rd Class coaches, a 2nd Class coach, and last the van. Friend said that he collected tickets from the fore-part of the train, from the 1st and 3rd Class carriages, while Alexander Ingles took the others. Morris joined Friend at the 3rd Class carriage, next to the first. Friend told the Court of Inquiry that he did not collect tickets from all the passengers on the train as some were season ticket holders.

There was nothing out of the ordinary about the train that night to attract Friend's attention. He paid no attention to the driver, nor did he see the guard. There was nothing about the way in which the train was marshalled or the mode in which it approached Friend's ticket-collecting box that was at all calculated to excite attention more than upon any other occasion. All about his collecting-box was in its usual order; as was the line.

Alexander Ingles was the porter at St Fort. He commonly assisted in the collection of tickets when a train arrived, though only from passengers going to Dundee. He agreed with Friend that the Edinburgh train had arrived bang on time. Ingles carried out his ticket-collecting duties and handed the tickets to Friend.

Robert Morris was the Station Master at St Fort station, He too participated in collecting tickets, and handed them to Friend, whose business it was to keep them. There was nothing out of the ordinary when the train left St Fort, and Morris had no reason to anticipate that there would be any difference with that train from any other train that had crossed the bridge since it had been built.

James Smith was the Station Master at what was known as the Taybridge station at Dundee. He had worked for the North British Railway Company for 25 years and had been at Taybridge station since the bridge had been opened. Prior to that he had held office in Burntisland, and at both places he had been the Station Master.

It was part of Smith's duty as Station Master to be present at the station on Sunday at any time, and he was there on Sunday 28 December, from about 6.30pm. He was not there, however, as part of his ordinary duty – he was there in consequence of the locomotive foreman, James Moyes, having come to his house to tell him that it was blowing a terrible gale outside, so much so that it was driving loaded wagons from the back of the viaduct at the Dundee end along to the middle of the goods yard.

Smith had never experienced a storm as bad as the one that night. He had also never seen the bridge oscillating, either under the wind or from any other cause, although he had been on it when the wind had been blowing very strongly, both walking and on a train. None of the guards or the driver of the train at any time intimated to Smith that in their opinion the bridge was in any way unsafe.

When Smith went to the station he found the facts to be as Moyes had represented: three wagons, coupled together, had been displaced, and had been driven along in an easterly direction some 300 to 400 yards by the violence of the storm. Smith had never seen the wind driving loaded wagons such a distance, seeing that there was an ascending gradient the way they were coming. Each of these wagons was loaded with coal and they averaged about 10 gross tons each. Smith did not replace the wagons, but only scotched them, so that they would not roll any further.

Smith thought the violence of the storm was such that it was likely to blow the roof off the station altogether and many parts of the roof were damaged – a great part of the glass roof was destroyed. Smith sent for his inspector, Robert Caird, and asked him to shut the gate of the exit stairs at Union Street Bridge to prevent passengers from coming down and passengers who were expected by train from going that way, as the roof was worst about that part. Smith was afraid of their being injured by any part of the roof falling.

A local Newport train, due to leave at 7.15pm, was standing in one of the dock sidings at the west end of the station, and Smith considered it would be dangerous for passengers to go along to where it was, and accordingly instructed his inspector to bring it back to the foot of the middle stairs, where the passengers could come down and get into the carriages without any risk. Smith made this arrangement with a view not only to the comfort but also to the safety of his expected passengers.

After he had made these arrangements, he looked to see how the signal stood with reference to the train that he was expecting shortly. By then it was about half past 7 o'clock. The signals were, he said, 'drawn', or showing clear, which indicated that permission had been given for a train to approach and that it had passed the south end of the bridge. The signals were never drawn until the train was signalled from the south end. Smith therefore expected that the Edinburgh train was at hand and expected its arrival at any moment. It was about 10 minutes after Smith noticed the signals that he felt uneasy about the train not having appeared. He saw a number of his own men standing on the platform, and called out and asked them if any of them could work the telegraph. Robert Shand, the guard of the last northbound train across the bridge, said he would do so.

Smith sent a messenger for the key of the telegraph office and, on going in, he asked Shand to put the question to the signalman at the south end as to whether the Edinburgh train had crossed the bridge. He found that none of the instruments would work. That led him to suspect that something very serious had happened: he thought that the high wind might have blown down some walls or something like that.

Finding that he could not communicate with the other side of the river, Smith left the office and met John Nelson, who had worked painting the bridge. Smith thought there was also another man there, but he did not know his name, although he did know the two gentlemen by sight. They told Smith what they had seen at the other end of the bridge: they had seen fire, they had seen the train enter onto the bridge, and a short time after they had seen some unusual fire falling, it seemed, from the top of the bridge to the water, which they supposed was from the train. Smith said it was a very serious matter and he hoped they should not spread the report of the fire. They were satisfied that something was wrong, and Nelson said he would go to the harbour-master.

Smith then sent for Shand again, told him the report that was being spread and ordered that all the entrances to the station to be shut, as there was likely to be a crowd and glass was falling from the roof. He then proceeded to the engine sheds, where he expected to find James Roberts, the locomotive foreman, and they went together onto the bridge, to the signal cabin at the north end. Smith did not see then that the bridge had given way, and they proceeded along it as far as they could. Then they saw there was a gap – they went far enough to see that the bridge was partly blown down. Smith returned with Roberts, and he arranged that he would go to the harbour-master and get a steamer at once

Thomas Barclay was the signalman at the south end of the Tay Bridge. He was 29 years old and had been a signalman for three years and eight months, ever since first joining the North British Railway Company. He had been the signalman on the Tay Bridge ever since it had been opened, and he told the Court that his responsibility as signalman was signalling the trains and operating the block telegraph, a communication system so arranged as to ensure that two trains were not on the same section of track at the same time.

On that Sunday night Barclay was on duty in his cabin, and his job was to pass the trains from Dundee and from St Fort in the afternoon and evening. As was his usual duty, he had to pass the train that was coming up from Edinburgh that day to St Fort at a few minutes past 7 o'clock. He got the signal that the train was approaching at 8 minutes past 7, that signal being given when the train left St Fort.

Before Barclay allowed the train to pass his cabin, he telegraphed at 7.09 to the north end to know if the line was clear. His telegraph signal was acknowledged, by first one beat of the bell, then two, then one. Having thus ascertained that the line was clear, Barclay gave the driver the single-line staff, or baton, to signify that the line was clear for his train to cross.

When the train passed Barclay's cabin he judged that it was travelling at the usual speed, that laid down in regulations for the bridge. Nothing about the train's speed was noteworthy. He also thought that there was nothing either in the company's servants or in the state of the train to attract his attention to the condition of the train more than usual.

When the train passed his cabin it was his duty to telegraph this fact to the north side by a bell-signal, and before he signalled it on he also gave the 'line clear' bell signal to the station in the rear, southwards.

Barclay recorded in his book the fact of the train passing his cabin, and then had to wait for any other train. He went to clean up his stove in the cabin, and prepared it to put on fresh fuel by raking out the ashes. He did not give the train a second thought after it had passed. As a general rule, trains would increase their speed after taking the baton, but Barclay had gone to attend to his other duties, so did not see further progress of this particular train.

John Watt, the foreman surfaceman, was with Barclay in his cabin that night. He had gone to the cabin with Barclay from their dwelling house at the side of the bridge. Watt was not there for any particular reason that night, but had been in the custom of going there. When the train arrived at Barclay's cabin Watt went out to it to give the driver the baton.

After it left Watt stood looking out of the cabin door window. The door was shut, but Watt was watching the train across the bridge, and after Barclay had done all his work and come up from the fire, Watt said that there was something wrong with the train – he was sure that he had seen a great flash of fire and the tail-lamps disappear.

Watt was not put about at all – he told Barclay what he had seen without any degree of excitement, but Barclay did not believe him. Barclay's impression was that the train was down the incline on the bridge, and he said they would watch and see it rounding the curve going into Dundee. Barclay waited a few seconds, then opened the door and went down to bring up some coal.

It was some 2½ or 3 minutes after Watt had said something was wrong before Barclay did anything in consequence of the disappearance of the tail-lights – they did not appear again. Barclay tried to ring the signalman at the north cabin to see whether he would answer him. He got no answer. Barclay had two speaking instruments with which he could communicate with the north cabin, both of which he tried. Finding that communication was cut, he then suspected that something had indeed gone wrong.

Barclay was struck for a moment, but soon afterwards he and Watt collected themselves and went outside. Barclay tried to get along the bridge a little, but the weather was so rough he and Watt were only able to get 20 or 30 yards along, so they retraced their steps back along the line and went along the Tayport branch, along the shore to the east. They had not proceeded northwards any further because the wind was very strong, making a loud whistling noise, and Watt thought they should get a better view from the shore side.

The wind had been very rough and unusually boisterous that night, but it never struck Barclay that there would be anything wrong with the bridge. His cabin was unaffected by the gale, being a little sheltered, but the wind was so strong that he could not have heard any creaking noise from the bridge.

Barclay and Watt went along the Tayport line with the aim of getting a better view of the bridge from the east. At first they could not see whether the bridge was complete or had been broken, it was so dark. They went backwards and forwards to each side, east and west of the bridge along the shore, to see if they could discover anything. Barclay first saw something on the east side of the bridge: the moon had come out and he therefore had a better view. He saw quite clearly that the bridge had given way.

The two men were not sure whether the train had arrived at Dundee, and decided to go and see if they could get any tidings at Newport. There they learned that the train had not arrived, so they went on to Tayport, where they saw the agent, and told him what they had seen.

Henry Somerville was the signalman stationed at the north end of the Tay Bridge, and had been there for 12 months, having previously been a signalman at Leuchars. He was therefore well accustomed to the signals used on the North British system. On Sunday 28th December he was on duty. He had begun his duty on the Saturday night until 10.30 on Sunday morning, then from 12.45pm to 2.30pm. After lunch he had resumed duty from 4 o'clock until 20 minutes to 11 on the Sunday night.

Somerville's signal box had two floors, with stairs from the lower to the upper part to raise him 10 or 15 feet above the level of the line, from which position, on an ordinary clear night, he could see a very long way across the bridge; he could even see the signals at the south cabin from the head of the stairs. However, on this occasion he could not see any further than a signal 1,200 yards distant; he could see the signal light at that distance but could not see any of its surroundings. Apart from that light, he could see nothing beyond about 50 yards from his stair head that night.

Somerville had never felt the bridge oscillating from stress of weather. He told the Court that during that day a number of passenger trains crossed the bridge: first there was a train south from Dundee at 7.30am, and another at 9.50am. In the afternoon there was a train at 12.50pm, one at 4.00pm and one at 4.10 pm. From the south there was a passenger train from Edinburgh at 6.20am, and trains from Tayport at 10.25am, 1.40pm and 5.50pm. Then the last train from Edinburgh was due at a few minutes past 7 o'clock.

Somerville observed that there was a wind all that day, although early on it was only a slight breeze, increasing towards the afternoon and evening. At 4.00pm the wind began to increase with considerable violence, and by 7.00pm it was a perfect hurricane. It was the worst weather he had seen since he had first come to the bridge. He felt it in his cabin, which was very much exposed to it. Somerville could hear nothing but the wind, which was very loud, whistling round about him. At 6.30pm the chimney cairn of the cabin blew off, and his cabin shook slightly. At the time that the 4 o'clock and the 4.10pm southbound trains were passing, the wind had risen so as to be very violent. However, it did not cross Somerville's mind that the bridge might be in danger.

Later that evening Somerville was in his cabin expecting the arrival of the train from Edinburgh, which was due at the south cabin at 7.11pm. Its booked time to cross the bridge was 5 minutes, so it should have arrived at the north cabin at 7.16pm. Slightly early, he got a signal from the south cabin at 7.09pm offering him the Edinburgh train. This did not mean that the train was at the south cabin or on the bridge, but that it had reached St Fort, the last stopping-place before the bridge; the object was to ensure that the line ahead of the train was clear. Somerville recorded this time in his book, as he always did. The next telegraph bell message he received, informing him that the train was on the bridge, was at 7.14pm; it had passed the south cabin, so he expected it up within 5 minutes.

Somerville waited 9 minutes for the coming train before he began to wonder at its non-appearance. He then went to the top of the cabin stairs to look out along the bridge to see if he could see anything of it. The wind was then blowing very strongly. He saw nothing of the coming train – he could not see far along the bridge, only to the Distant signal some 1,200 yards from his box. Somerville would have seen the train's lights at that distance if it had been on the line, but he did not see them. Nor did he see the signal. He thought this meant that the signal light was out, perhaps blown out by the wind, although he had never seen that happen before.

Somerville did not see the train, nor did he hear any noise of the crash of the bridge giving way or the train going over into the water. He thought, in retrospect, that those events must have happened with considerable noise, but the violence of the wind had prevented him from hearing anything. He tried the speaking instrument provided for communication with the cabin on the south side, but found that it was disconnected. He therefore tried the bell, and found that that would not work either. Becoming very anxious he went out to the top of the stairs again. He knew that something very serious had happened. The train had not appeared and communication had been disconnected, so he went out again to see if he could see the train. He saw nothing.

Two gentlemen on the esplanade spoke to Somerville and informed him that the bridge had gone down. The combination of this information and the breakdown in communications made Somerville get in touch with James Roberts, the locomotive foreman, whom he found at the engine shed. Having told Roberts how matters stood, he returned to his signal box, where he remained until 10.40pm. That was the time he was due to leave work, and he did so.

6
PASSENGERS

*'I formed the opinion that they always
drove across the bridge very carefully.'*

A number of passengers on the Tay Bridge line were very vigilant travellers. They kept detailed records of the progress of trains they were travelling in, noting arrival and departure times, and calculating speeds. They were therefore in a good position to confirm whether there was a culture of excessive speed among drivers on the line that might have contributed to the fate of the train that night.

John Leng was the managing proprietor and editor of the *Dundee Advertiser*. He lived at Newport, so had to cross the river twice a day, and had begun to do this journey by the Tay Bridge from its opening. During the last two or three months of the year he crossed the river on an average of three times daily in each direction, making one of the six crossings by ferry. He had a composition or contract (season) ticket by boat, which expired on 17 November; from a preference his family had for travelling by train, he then changed the ticket for a corresponding railway ticket. From then his family almost invariably used the train for the journey into Dundee. As well as using the composition ticket he also bought single tickets for himself by the ferries – he wished to have a choice of route.

Occasionally, in trains coming from the south to the north, Leng thought the speed exceeded what he understood to be the regulation 25mph, although he had never timed the journey watch in hand. The impression from merely casual observation was that the speed was occasionally above 25mph.

Leng had found it difficult to form a very accurate impression of the speed of trains on account of the flashing light between the latticework and the girders, so he never expressed himself strongly, because he had the impression that the passing of the lattices possibly produced a feeling that the train was going faster than it really was.

Sometimes it was Leng's impression that the trains were going at more than 30 or 40mph, and at that speed there was motion in the carriage that attracted his attention, a motion that was not ordinarily felt on a level railway, a railway on land, on solid ground, running on a dead level. Leng considered that the motion was a prancing motion, involving a rise and fall. It felt like going down a steep incline in a hilly district, such as on the Caledonian line in Dumfriesshire or the North Western Railway in the neighbourhood of Kendal.

Leng also experienced another motion, a lateral motion; he had repeatedly felt a motion from side to side, but could not say whether it was the motion of the bridge. He rather felt, at the time, that it was the motion of the carriage, and was very similar – neither greater nor less – to that which was felt in all trains going at speed. Leng connected this motion with the speed at which the trains were running. However, the speed and the motion thereby produced created in Leng's mind no concern at all – he never felt any apprehension whatever with regard to the safety of the bridge, although he thought there might be danger if any casualty occurred to the train itself. It was only from hearing others expressing some anxiety on the subject with regard to themselves and the members of their families that he mentioned the speed to two officers of the railway; some ladies had complained to Leng about the speed, and that had led him to speak to railway officers. Leng believed that a complaint had been made by former Provost Robertson when the ladies of his family had complained about the velocity of the trains. Leng did not remember that the ladies of his own family ever expressed any fear regarding the bridge, or expressed any opinion with regard to the speed.

Leng communicated with Smith, the Station Master, and Noble, who was an inspector of the bridge, about his concerns regarding the speed of some trains. He told Smith that he and Robertson had conversed about it, and that Leng also understood that some ladies were in a state of apprehension on the subject.

Leng had always found the Station Master exceedingly attentive and obliging when he had spoken to him on any subject. Having spoken to him twice on the subject of the speed of the trains, Smith promised him that he would look into the matter and give it his attention. The Station Master mentioned to the signalman to keep a record of the passing of the trains.

Leng also voiced his concerns to Noble. In crossing over in a boat late one evening with Noble, he mentioned to him that Robertson and he had been speaking about the velocity of the trains. He suggested to him that he might inquire of Bouch whether or not it would be practicable to have an automatic register at each of the signal cabins that would record the passing of every train from end to end. Noble said he would bring the suggestion to Bouch's notice, which he duly did.

Invariably Leng had felt the motion he had described when trains were travelling in one direction, from south to north. He could not say that travelling from north to south it existed: it must have been only very slightly perceptible, if at all, otherwise he thought he would have noticed it.

As a newspaper man, Leng had many opportunities of speaking upon the subject of the bridge and its safety with people in Newport. He found it difficult to speak of general impressions but he knew, when going over in a train, that a fellow passenger would remark 'the train seems to be going very fast' or 'faster than usual'. However, Leng did not hear such remarks very often, although he did hear them on more than one occasion, probably five or six times during the whole time he travelled across the bridge. On his second communication with Noble about the speed of the trains, Leng wished to ascertain from him that his views had been represented to Bouch. These conversations had taken place in the latter part of December, very shortly before the bridge went down.

The trains habitually slowed as they approached the south cabin for the purpose of taking up the baton, and afterwards the speed rapidly and noticeably increased coming northwards. Leng was struck on several occasions how quickly the speed increased, and it reached its maximum through the high girders. Leng particularly noticed that the local Newport trains gained speed very rapidly; these were local trains, pulled by a small tank engine.

On other lines Leng had observed a similar phenomenon to that experienced on the Tay Bridge – a prancing of the carriages upon the rails. This prancing might have been the movement of the carriages on the rails while the rails themselves remained rigid. He had not observed this prancing motion on the long trains, the through trains, but only in the case of the local Newport trains. These were much lighter than the through trains, not having as many carriages; also the carriages were often not as full, so were not as heavy either in the number of the vehicles or in the character of the loads they carried. Leng inferred from his observations that such a prancing would be more likely to take place in a short and light train than in a long and heavy train. However, at the same time a short and light train would be less apt to move the bridge vertically than a long, heavy train.

Leng's observation was therefore quite consistent with there not having been a movement up and down of the structure of the bridge. He had, however, travelled over a considerable number of bridges, and did not remember having felt the same sensation elsewhere. He had even travelled on the American continent where trains travelled over a number of bridges of greater length than were common in Great Britain, and the Tay Bridge was the only case where he had experienced such a motion when travelling on a short, light, local train across such a structure. His impression was certainly that the unusual motion was produced by the passing of the train across the bridge, which would not have been produced if the train had been passing over a solid base. He again likened it to that experienced on a very steep incline, a peculiar prancing motion that increased when the trains had acquired a greater velocity and the brake had to be put on. Leng felt this prancing motion when a train was passing through the high girders, where the bridge was nearly level. The train seemed always to attain its greatest speed through the high girders, and the greater the speed, the more the prancing motion was perceptible.

Captain William Robertson was an engineer by training and lived at Newport, where he had been the provost of the burgh from 1875 to 1878. He was harbour-master of Dundee, and as such superintended the diving operations to ascertain the condition of the wrecked bridge and train (see Chapter 9). He also gave evidence to the Court of Inquiry as an eye-witness (see Chapter 2).

As we have already seen, Robertson had observed the speed at which passenger trains ran across the bridge on various occasions, timing them from shore to shore. He also timed trains through the high girders. Robertson understood that trains were limited to 25mph on any part of the bridge, and under ordinary circumstances he did not think that there was more cause for apprehension of danger arising from the speed of a train within the high girders than on those parts to the north and south of them.

The ease with which trains travelled at the two ends of the bridge had produced no uncomfortable feeling in Robertson's mind as a passenger, and therefore gave him no concern. The reason he observed the speed within the girders was from the fact that the speed at that particular point did produce some discomfort and concern. He once timed the train at 4 minutes 20 seconds from signal box to signal box, and since the length of the bridge from box to box was about 2 miles he therefore thought the train was running slightly in excess of 25mph from box to box. This speed occasioned very much discomfort in Robertson; he detected that there was a very perceptible vertical vibration, and also a very perceptible lateral vibration upon the bridge with the train running at that kind of speed, and when the train was within the girders it was running at a higher speed than average.

Robertson thought that by the time the train reached the high girders it would have attained the speed it had at the south box. Therefore, although the train was going in excess of 25mph from shore to shore, the actual speed in the high girders was greater than that average.

Even after making his complaint about speed to Station Master Smith, Robertson noticed that the trains still maintained a speed that he thought dangerous. His complaint had not resulted in what he had desired to bring about, so he had simply given up using the railway from south to north.

As we have already heard, Robertson only once took observation of the time from cabin to cabin. The Aberdeen express was late one night, and the local Newport train, timed to leave Newport at 7.13pm, was detained until the express had crossed the bridge. When the Newport train approached the south end of the bridge, it braked on approaching the cabin to allow the driver to take the baton from the signalman, but the fact that it approached the cabin with more speed than usual induced Robertson to take out his watch to time the train from that cabin to the other.

He did not think that the train going from south to north usually took delivery of the baton when moving at a speed of more than 4 or 6mph, but as he had only begun to use the train from south to north on 4 November and ceased to do so around the middle of December he did not have enough experience of travelling to be able to say that anything happened on the line 'usually'. However, he was perfectly certain that the train passed the south cabin at a speed between 4 and 8mph, and it picked up the baton when so travelling during all the time he travelled on the line. This view was based on his observation of the train, as he did not time it from the south cabin until it entered the high girders.

Not all Robertson's observations were based upon travel by the local Newport train; he also included among his observations trains coming from St Andrews. He did not know what kinds of engines were used on these local trains, despite being an engineer himself, although he knew that a small tank engine had a much smaller driving wheel than the engines that ran the longer distances. He was not aware that the object of the small driving wheels of tank engines was to get up a moderate speed quickly on starting such local trains – he had never thought of that. He also did not know what speed those tank engines could attain, and did not think there was a continuous brake on any of these trains; he thought it was just the ordinary brake.

Robertson had distinguished the ease with which he had traversed the bridge at each end, by contrast with the discomfort in the middle. Taking the high girders as the point of observation, he found that the slow and easy travelling continued substantially until he entered the single girders, but was worse in the high girders, because the speed was being constantly increased until the train reached the summit.

Robertson could not very well tell what the limit of distance of the vertical vibration had been. He could not indicate any measurement, and he could not very easily describe the impression that the vertical vibration produced upon his mind. However, he observed the train lifting bodily from the rails, leaping from the rails in a sort of bounding motion.

He believed that trains more frequently approached the south cabin at a greater speed than 3mph. He had made many observations from the steamer's deck, where he was in a position to make a perfectly correct observation of the speed of trains. Nothing, either in the position of the steamer or his position on board it, hindered him from being as accurate as if he was in the train. He observed the movement both vertically and laterally in the bridge as a result of the train crossing it.

Robertson did not have any doubt that the vertical movement was a result of the bridge's movement, and the bouncing motion he had seen was one that would not have happened on solid ground. It resembled the spring or swing that might be felt in walking along a suspension bridge, and was always markedly so at those high speeds, but only at those high speeds, particularly going from south to north. He had observed these high speeds in trains going in both directions, but to a much lesser extent in the trains going south than in the trains coming north. It was very marked at a speed of about 35mph, and it was still more marked with a time of 50 seconds in the high girders, representing a speed of 42.92mph. This indicated to Robertson that the movement he detected was greater when trains were travelling at higher speeds.

Robertson thought the vertical movement in trains moving at 35.78mph sufficient to attract the attention of any intelligent passenger; most people would have been quite sensible to it at that speed, even if they could attribute no cause to it.

The lateral movement of the trains he always attributed to the movement of the bridge, and it too increased in proportion to the rate of progress of the trains; this speed increased sufficiently to indicate that the rate of progression was a serious matter in considering the safety of the bridge. The movement of the bridge was definitely perceptible, though Robertson could not put any accurate measurement to its extent, whether 1 or 2 inches, just that it was a movement much beyond anything he had ever experienced in a train progressing on solid ground. Robertson had no doubt that it was the movement of the bridge and not merely the movement of the train.

Thomas Baxter was a commission agent in the Royal Exchange, Dundee. He lived at West Newport, where his house overlooked the bridge, and he had a good view of it, all except the southernmost high girder. He was a regular passenger on the bridge, although he did not hold a season ticket. He had been using the bridge since it had opened, doing the journey perhaps twice a week.

Baxter recalled having travelled over with former Provost William Robertson one day in December, the month of the disaster. Robertson had taken out his pocket watch to time the journey from passing the south cabin until they passed the north cabin. He had sat looking at his watch the whole time. He did not speak. He simply took out his watch and looked at it. Baxter had a shrewd idea why Robertson was timing the train. Robertson had timed that journey at 4 minutes 20 seconds, which made Baxter notice more particularly the speed of the train. He had not felt any discomfort until they got within the girders, but then he felt alarmed at the speed of the train, gauged from the girders, which were flashing past. However, he did not notice any vibration; in fact, before that evening his attention had never been drawn to the speed of any train, and he would never have been afraid to cross the bridge.

At Dundee Baxter went with Robertson to meet Smith, the Station Master, as they were leaving the station. Robertson complained to Smith about the speed, and said that it was not right that the engine driver should be allowed to make up his speed upon the bridge. Smith was very anxious to get statistics from Robertson, and expressed great regret that there should be any complaint about the speed of trains.

Dr James Miller was a doctor of medicine, practising in Dundee. He lived in Tay Street, Dundee, and pretty frequently had occasion to cross the Tay Bridge, visiting patients on the south side. This he had been doing over the whole period of its existence.

On two or three dozen occasions Miller had timed the speed of the train passing through the high girders, watch in hand, from simple curiosity. The fastest time he ever noted was 50 seconds, and that was only once. In contrast, on another occasion he distinctly recollected the train crossing in 72 seconds, which was about the longest time he had ever observed; he had timed trains more often over 60 seconds than under.

During his journeys, Miller had not noticed any vibration or oscillation more than on any other line, and never observed anything particular in the motion of one kind or another to call his attention to it. Those trains going north went at a higher speed than those going south, although he had only timed trains coming north.

Duncan MacDonald was a magistrate in Dundee, and very frequently crossed the Tay Bridge, both by the Newport train and by the through trains. This he had been doing from the time the bridge had opened until it fell, crossing at least two or three times a week.

MacDonald would pay attention to the speed of the trains on which he was travelling, which he did by observing it both without his watch and also with his watch, both ways. He was told, before he crossed, that the trains took about 5 minutes. He did not expect that, and therefore curiosity led him to start timing his journeys. When he first did this, he was going from the north to the south, but not from station to station, nor was the timing done from cabin to cabin. MacDonald made it his rule to look until he saw the water below, so that he counted from one side of the water to the other side, which was a little less than from cabin to cabin. In going across on the first day he timed the train it took a little over 7 minutes from north to south.

On coming from the south to the north MacDonald timed the train from the moment he saw the water under him until he saw the land. He timed the journey in this direction at least a dozen times, and only timed it at less than 5½ minutes on one occasion. MacDonald could not remember whether it was a Newport or a St Andrews train on the Newport line, but he had calculated the journey at a second or two within 5 minutes. He did not think there was any material increase in speed within the high girders as compared with the rest of the journey, although there definitely was a very slight increase. The trains seemed to him, at least coming from the south, to have attained their full speed about two-thirds of the distance from the south end until they came to the high girders, and the increase in speed, if any, was quite immaterial, to his thinking.

MacDonald did not believe that at any part of his journey did the train ever go at 40mph. At no time did he ever perceive any vibration or oscillation, either vertical or lateral. He always felt safe crossing the whole of the bridge and frequently spoke of it as being the easiest and smoothest part of the line. There was never anything that occurred to him to excite either any apprehension or misgiving as to its stability or safety.

MacDonald thought that 5 minutes would indicate 24mph, calculating the bridge at 2 miles in length, although the distance was in fact a little less. He was not sure exactly what the highest speed at which he had travelled had been, but judging by observations of distance on the land he did not believe it could ever have exceeded 25 or 26mph.

He explained the sensation of high speed as the rapidity at which the girders flashed past his eyes, which would be apparent to anybody who travelled in a railway carriage. When the line opened it was, of course, the talk of everybody. A day or two before he had begun to make his experiments he had heard people speaking of the speed of the trains. It was on a Saturday that the line had opened, and on the following Saturday he crossed for the first time. People had been talking to him as to the very great convenience it would afford, saying that now trains would cross and did cross in about 5 minutes, and curiosity led him to time his journeys. The very first day he travelled he timed the train and continued to do so occasionally until the last. He was not sure if he timed it during the last week before he travelled for the final time on Monday 22nd. He had never heard any complaint that the speed on the bridge might have been excessive, until after it fell.

George Hume was a ships' stores merchant in Dundee, and lived in Newport. He had been doing the journey between Newport and Dundee on the ferry before the bridge opened, and thereafter became a regular passenger across the bridge in both directions. He crossed twice each way every day, from the date it had opened on 31 May, with a few exceptions, including the day the bridge fell.

As a matter of curiosity Hume had occasionally taken the times of trains. While he could not remember the exact times trains on which he had been travelling had taken to cross the bridge, he thought broadly that they had taken from 5 to 6 minutes from cabin to cabin. Hume was frequently of the opinion that the trains he was on were going at a high speed, especially over the centre of the bridge. He had only once timed the train passing through the high girders, and on that occasion it had passed through at 35mph; this was some two months before the bridge fell. He had timed the train on that day because he found that it was getting up speed pretty quickly, and as a matter of curiosity he took out his watch before it entered the girders. The train was not, in his view, going faster than usual as it approached the south cabin, but as it was approaching the high girders Hume thought that they were getting up an unusual speed. He did not, however, feel any vibration, and there was nothing to disturb him or alarm him upon that occasion. He thought the train could have gone more quickly without any danger, unless from the breaking of an axle – that was the only thing that was ever present to his mind.

Hume thus had perfect confidence in the stability of the bridge, his only fear arising from the extra speed being an accident to the train itself. He continued to travel with the same confidence with which he had travelled from the first, and never felt any vibration. When a train went through the girders there was a sort of flashing from passing through the latticework so near the carriage windows, which might strike people who were not accustomed to it. However, he was not aware that it was an unusual thing to have such latticework so near the carriage windows.

Alexander Hutchinson was an architect in Dundee who lived in Broughty Ferry. The summer before the bridge fell he had been working in Tayport and Newport, and had frequently crossed the Tay Bridge, probably twice a week, once in each direction. He did this journey from about April until the beginning of September.

Hutchinson frequently took advantage of these journeys to time the trains, taking the time precisely from cabin to cabin by the second hand on his watch. While he had not made any notes of the times when he was on the bridge, nevertheless he had a perfect recollection of them.

As a rule Hutchinson found that trains travelled faster from south to north, markedly so. He timed the trains with his watch in his hand, and ordinarily he found that the journey took between 4 and 4½ minutes from cabin to cabin; on one occasion, at the beginning of September, he had timed the journey at 3½ minutes.

On the Saturday before the bridge went down Hutchinson timed the train from south to north at 4 minutes from cabin to cabin; this was a fast train that had stopped at St Fort station. The other trains were local trains, the Tayport trains – it had been a local train that had crossed in 3½ minutes. Hutchinson thought that the speed of that train had been too great, and the direct result of the speed of these crossings was that he gave up using the Tayport train at the beginning of September.

When Hutchinson found that the main-line trains were also, in his opinion, going too fast, he resolved not to use the train again from south to north; he did not know that he made a resolution to that effect, but he thought that he should have to give it up. It was not very easy giving up the train when he had to go to other places that there were no other means of reaching, but he felt uncomfortable.

After that time, therefore, he would not take the train by choice if he had other means – the speed made him mentally, although not physically, uncomfortable, and he apprehended risk or danger from the movement of the girders. He had experienced motion in the train, which he attributed to the motion of the bridge, and had felt it more markedly through the high girders than outside. That motion was both vertical and lateral: he thought the vertical motion was quite noticeable, much more so than the lateral – he likened it to a distinct bounding movement. He felt as if the carriage floor rose up beneath him, just as, sometimes in coming to the foot of an incline, one might feel a sort of impulse while the train seemed to rise.

Hutchinson felt the same motion coming through the high girders to such an extent as to make him uneasy. At the time he attributed this motion to the motion of the bridge, which produced a great motion in the train, and he thought that it was increased by the speed at which the train was going. It was less, not so perceptible, when the train was going from north to south.

To get to the summit of the bridge from Dundee any train had to get up a considerable gradient, so they could not get up speed towards the summit in the same way as they could from the south of the bridge towards the high girders. Practically, the bridge was on a level between the south box and the high girders, but the gradient on the north was much more marked – it was very obvious to the naked eye from the north side to the summit of the bridge.

Hutchinson had been using the bridge from its opening, and thought that both the oscillation and vibration were more marked in his later experience than at first. He imagined that the movements were mainly due to the increased speed of the trains. It also occurred to him that the oscillation or vibration – especially the oscillation – of the bridge arose from it getting looser than it had been when it was originally constructed. However, his view was that the primary cause of the movement – both vertical and horizontal – was the excessive speed at which the train was travelling, and that the vertical motion was even greater than the lateral motion. When he had first experienced this vertical motion of the bridge it had impressed itself on his mind as leading to the risk of danger.

Hutchinson had not used the Tayport train since the beginning of September, but before that he had been going by train to Tayport from north to south, then on his return journey leaving the train at Newport and taking the steamer. Previously he had never been in the habit of doing that, only having done so occasionally when the train did not suit.

The difference between what Hutchinson had felt on solid ground and what he had felt on the bridge was great. The floor of the carriage rose up and went away again just as if one was bounding, and this he attributed, whether rightly or wrongly, to the vertical vibration of the bridge; the extent of vibration he felt was more than an inch. As regards the lateral movement, he had difficulty in distinguishing how much of that was attributable to movement of the carriage, and how much to the movement of what the carriage was travelling upon.

His experience was that latterly trains had been travelling faster than when he had first travelled on the line. He had never complained to any of the officials on the subject as he had never found the benefits of making complaints at any time; his experience of complaints to public companies had not been favourable. He had complained about other matters, many times, but had certainly never suggested to any of the officials of the company that the bridge was getting loose – he would need to have been convinced before taking such a step. All he could be definite about was the mere fact of the oscillations being repeated on that bridge having a tendency to loosen it.

He thought it was perfectly fair that railway officials had been going along the bridge constantly, and they should have been aware of this oscillation, or looking for its causes: if the bridge was loosening, it was their business to look after it. However, there was no doubt that, if he had thought the bridge had loosened to such an extent as to produce an immediate danger, he would have felt it his duty to have spoken upon the subject.

Hutchinson thought there were other dangers as well. There was the danger of the Tayport train starting off at such a speed after leaving the south end. However, that was a matter that should have been easily discernible by the railway officials if they had been attending to their duty. Hutchinson therefore thought there was no use in complaining because they ought to have been cognisant of it – after all, registers were kept at the ends of the bridge.

Hutchinson had been making a note of the time taken to cross the bridge every time he had noticed movement, and his timings were broadly the same as those of William Robertson mentioned above. He had found that, from north to south, trains went across in 4½ to 5 minutes, and coming over in the other direction between 4 and 4½ minutes. However, the time taken from cabin to cabin had on one occasion been 3½ minutes, which was the greatest speed he ever observed. He found the worst oscillation mainly within the high girders, and felt it on approaching them from the south; he felt it begin before he entered the high girders and it continued all the way through, being fairly even all through that distance. Hutchinson could scarcely say whether there was any difference between the middle of the girders and the piers, except that the piers did not go up and down.

James McAllen was also an architect in Dundee, and was the proprietor of an estate at Berry Bank at Cupar, Fife, where he and his family lived. He had travelled on the line since the opening of the bridge until the day before it fell, crossing daily at least once each way. He generally travelled by the through train, and occasionally by the local or Newport train.

On McAllen's journeys he had good opportunities to observe the speeds at which both the through and local trains ran, and he formed the opinion that trains always drove across the bridge very carefully both ways. His conviction was that they never occupied less than 5 minutes in crossing the bridge proper; however, he never timed a train with his watch.

McAllen generally travelled by the 4.05pm train from Dundee, and sometimes by another train that left for Newport at 4 o'clock, and as always both were despatched very punctually. The 4.05 train had invariably to slow and sometimes to come to a full stop at the north cabin before being allowed to go on the bridge, because the train that had left 5 minutes earlier was not clear of the bridge. McAllen's train had often to wait 2 minutes, and the passengers naturally wondered what the delay was. McAllen always made it his practice to look out for the Newport train getting off the bridge. Practically, there was no difference in speed, so far as he could judge, between the trains going either way.

There was nothing in the speed at any time either way to excite the slightest apprehension in his mind. It never occurred to him that the speed was reckless or dangerous, and he observed no difference whatever between the speeds when the bridge had first opened and latterly. On the bridge he never felt as much oscillation or vibration, whether vertical or lateral, as upon the other parts of the line beyond the bridge at any time between the opening and the fall of the bridge. In fact, he thought it was rather improved after the bridge had been opened for a time. Drivers were rather more careful and punctual latterly than they had been at first, having become more accustomed to the bridge. At first drivers were apt to draw up suddenly when they were going to get the baton, but latterly they went on quite smoothly and drivers seemed to adjust their speed. The management of the trains was much better: to pick up or deliver the baton on the south side the train came down very slowly and there was a man always ready to catch the baton from the signalman as the train passed.

McAllen did observe some oscillation and vibration, but these were those little usual waverings that he set down to the giving of the springs under the ordinary movement in railway trains. This never struck him as any different from other railway bridges he had travelled on. He thought that there was nothing whatever connected with his experience to excite apprehension or misgiving. Having crossed the bridge daily, he had experienced it in all kinds of weather, sometimes a little squally and cold.

He normally did his morning journey by the through train, and in his experience there was no vibration whatever in the bridge, more than on an ordinary line, other than that occasioned by the carriage. He was convinced that any oscillation or vibration was due to the carriage, and not to the bridge in any degree.

Herman Quosbarth was the German Empire's part-time consul in Dundee. He was 50 years old and lived in Fernbrae near Newport, on the south side of the Tay. He worked for Quosbarth & Petersen, a firm of shipbrokers on Castle Street in Dundee, and crossed the bridge daily, travelling between home and work from the time the bridge was opened for traffic until it fell. He had taken out his composition ticket in May 1879, when the Newport branch was opened, and would travel by the morning train to Dundee and by the afternoon train back to Newport.

He had therefore been able to observe the speed at which trains ran across the bridge, and had experienced no trouble. He found the line remarkably smooth to travel on, and the time from Newport to Dundee was almost always kept within 10 minutes. He had found that if the train was sometimes a little late, perhaps by a minute or two, the driver was sure to get to Dundee in time. Although it might have varied occasionally, he had found that the interval of time specified was preserved between the two places.

Nothing had ever struck Quosbarth as undue or excessive about the trains' speed. Occasionally, the morning train, leaving Newport at 8.35am, would be a little quicker. Quosbarth had never timed the journey with a watch – it was too short – but he was aware what travelling at a speed of 40mph was like and had never travelled at anything near that speed on the bridge. He was certain of that. He had never been sensible of any vibration on the bridge; the only point he had remarked upon had been when sometimes there was an old carriage that was not as pleasant to travel in as a new one, when there was the ordinary shaking.

Quosbarth had not been conscious of any lateral vibration or oscillation, or any movement from side to side; indeed, his experience had been the reverse, that there was not anything of the sort. He had never found anything to do with the bridge to excite any fear in his mind or misgiving. He had perfect confidence in the bridge until it fell. He was sure that he would have felt anything excessive with regard to vibration, but there was nothing in the vibration to call special attention to it.

Quosbarth had never heard any complaint with regard to the speed of the trains, and never went at a speed of 40mph. The highest speed he had ever travelled in a train had been when he went by the 'Flying Scotsman', and had never crossed the bridge at that speed.

Henry Robertson was a merchant in Dundee and lived at Eden Grove, near Dairsie. He travelled by the Tay Bridge between Dundee and home daily, from the opening of the bridge until Christmas Day 1879. Occasionally, besides going by the train direct to Dairsie he went by the Tayport or Newport train.

Robertson accordingly had an opportunity of seeing the speed at which the trains travelled. He had noticed nothing in particular about them, although occasionally, when he had gone to Glasgow or Edinburgh, enquiries were made of him as to how long the train took to cross the bridge. Out of curiosity, so that he would be able to answer enquiries, he had timed a train two or three times, by his watch, from cabin to cabin, and had found it to be between 5 and 6 minutes, both ways. It did not strike him that there was any material difference in times between trains in each direction, but he did not time them in order to make comparisons. He did not think that that speed was too great. He had absolutely no doubt or misgiving as to the safety of the bridge, from its opening to the last date on which he used it.

Robertson never found any vibration or oscillation of the bridge to alarm him in any way, not so much as on many parts of the permanent way on solid land. Such movement as he detected in the trains he did not attribute to the bridge. He gave no thought as to what might be the cause of the vibrations he was feeling while on the bridge.

7
OBSERVERS OF THE WEATHER
IN THE TAY ESTUARY

'The river was running very high: it was a sheet of foam.'

This book is based on the evidence sessions given to the Court of Inquiry, but it might be useful, before dealing with those sessions covering the weather in the Tay that night, to examine an assessment of the weather patterns the night the bridge went down given by a contemporary meteorologist.

The storm of 28 December 1879 was described by A. Buchan, writing in the *Journal of the Scottish Meteorological Society* the year after the disaster, as having presented peculiarities that, taken together, made it one of the most remarkable storms yet observed in the British Isles. The most remarkable of these peculiarities was a barometric fluctuation that was of an extraordinary character along or near the central track of the storm from south-east to west.

These readings were recorded at a lighthouse in the Tay estuary, and Buchan observed that such extraordinary fluctuations were not isolated phenomena. That was shown by the readings at other lighthouses in that part of Scotland, at each of which it was the practice of the lighthouse-keepers to note, in addition to the regular 9.00am and 9.00pm observations, the lowest point to which the barometer fell and the time that it occurred.

Readings gave the progress of the storm in miles per hour. Between 4 and 5pm the wind was blowing at 30mph, between 5 and 6pm it was 45mph, between 6 and 7pm it was 53mph, and between 7 and 9pm it was 70mph. The rate of progress from 7 to 9pm was thus recorded at, according to Buchan, 3½ times the average progressive rate of storms in this part of Europe.

Buchan observed that the maximum temperature of the day marked the crest of a heat wave that accompanied the storm. Everywhere on the mainland of Scotland the temperature rose from 51°F to 57°, and it was further remarkable that the higher of these temperatures occurred at the more inland stations. In other words, the temperature in Scotland rose on this December day to the same average temperature for the first week of June.

Wind speeds were also observed to be high elsewhere in Scotland. At the Glasgow and Aberdeen Observatories on the evening of 29 December, wind speeds of up to 52mph were recorded between 8.50pm and 9.50pm. Taking shorter periods than 60 minutes, traces showed still greater velocities, ranging up to 120mph. Similarly, at Aberdeen, from 7.15pm to 7.20pm a wind speed of 96mph was registered. James Ewing, a lighthouse-keeper whose recordings of the weather that night were used by Buchan, wrote that 'the hurricane burst upon us with terrific force, and during four hours the lighthouse was buried in spray. The spray struck the lantern (145 feet above high water) with a sound like that which would have been produced by road metal.'

At the Tay Bridge the wind was in the west, or at right angles to the bridge, and in all probability its force was further intensified by the shape of the channel between the ranges of the hills through which the Tay flowed seawards. The Tay Bridge was situated at a narrow part of a long wide valley surrounded on both sides by hills.

Buchan observed that Mr McKelvie, the Scottish Meteorological Society's Observer at Dundee, had carefully collected information regarding the effects of the storm by personally visiting the localities. McKelvie was called by the Court of Inquiry, and his evidence is given below.

Some thousands of trees at Rossie Priory, 6 miles west of Dundee, were blown down on the night of the storm, leaving a clear space through the woods. Many trees were uprooted, and many others were snapped across at heights varying from 3 to 50 feet above the ground. Many of the prostrated trees were 9 feet in circumference and several of much larger girth. A beech tree 15 feet in circumference growing about 2 miles from the bridge was torn up by the roots and its six branches, each about 9 feet in girth springing from the trunk at a height 20 feet above the ground, were twisted like ropes.

In the eastern necropolis of Dundee, 20 monuments were overturned by the force of the storm and several large trees were thrown down in the neighbourhood. McKelvie drew attention to the strongest blasts recurring at intervals about 5 minutes apart, characterised by a strong and swirling lifting power accompanied at the same time with a cracking, shooting, rumbling noise in the upper air producing an impression as if it were descending towards the earth. This had also been a characteristic of the Edinburgh hurricane of 24 January 1868.

In connection with the strong swirling gusts of the storm, it was noted that the destruction to forests took place at different heights from the ground, as shown by the points at which the trees and branches were twisted and broken across. As the storm had passed over the greater part of Scotland by 9.00pm, the regular observing hour at the Society's stations, there was no very favourable opportunity of ascertaining the most pronounced movements of barometric pressure that occurred during the height of the storm.

Having dealt with a secondary account of the weather on the Tay that night, attention now turns to the first-hand accounts.

William McKelvie lived and worked in Dundee where he was a civil engineer and cemetery architect. Since 1852 he had kept a record of the weather there for the Scottish Meteorological Society. For this record, he noted the barometric and thermometric readings twice a day, at 9.00am and 9.00pm, at a height above the mean sea level of 167 feet. McKelvie did not, however, have an instrument to test wind pressure, and knew of no such instrument anywhere in Dundee. His observations he submitted to the Society monthly.

On Sunday 28 December, the morning of the day the bridge went down, his 9.00am barometer reading was 29.450psi (pounds per square inch), and at 9.00pm it was 28.990psi. At 9.00am the wind was south-westerly, blowing 1 – the strength of the wind he measured on a scale from 1 to 6, with 6 being the highest. At that time the wind was therefore at its lowest point. However, at 4 o'clock he did notice that there had been a considerable increase in the force, and at 5 o'clock he noticed that it was very much increased in force and velocity.

McKelvie had gone out to observe the wind a little before 6 o'clock, and it was blowing very hard. He had occasion then to walk a distance to church, and during that walk he was impressed with the peculiarity of the wind. It came on one occasion in gusts rather like a whirlwind, very strong, with a very concentrated force.

At some time past 8 o'clock he was sensible that the wind had diminished both in force and in velocity; the time between the swirls had increased from 5 to 7 minutes and the gusts were not so strong. At 9.00pm he recorded the wind at 6, the highest point on his scale, blowing north-west.

McKelvie was in church at half-past 6, and stayed there until 8 o'clock.

William Robertson was at the same service, but stayed until 9 o'clock. McKelvie was able to make observations of the wind while in church. One particular thing he noticed was the ventilator in the roof, which at one particular time made a tremendous noise, and McKelvie turned round to see what was wrong. He was afraid something had happened, and on looking round he feared it was the ventilator of the church that had blown off. He noticed the office-bearer going to fix it, and looking round he noticed that the time was 15 minutes past 7 by the church clock. He felt some insecurity at the time, but when he left church at 8 o'clock the wind had subsided considerably and the interval between the gusts had lengthened – there were now about 7 minutes between them.

After McKelvie left the church he went home, and on the way he encountered in the streets signs of violence from the results of the weather: broken chimney cairns, slates, zinc from the tops of houses and in one case a large door, blown off its hinges, a door with a latch on it. This alarmed him somewhat, both for his own safety and that of others passing along the streets.

Going home McKelvie was overtaken by some gentlemen who were in the church with him, and one of them said that he should have something to report about that night's gale to the Meteorological Society. One of them said he should not like to cross the bridge that night. That brought the bridge prominently into McKelvie's mind with reference to the gale, and when he got home it was still in his mind.

However, he had no fear for the stability of the bridge or anything on it. When he got home, at the foot of the street he met a gentleman who said to him that he had heard from a gentleman going to Invergowrie that the bridge was down. McKelvie said he had not heard it, and the gentleman said, 'I am going up the road to see.' McKelvie did not go with him, but went into his house.

Indoors he went upstairs and went to the window to see if he could see the bridge. He saw the near end of it, but the middle was under a sort of mist at the time. The moon was shining brightly and he saw the north end. For a short time the clouds therefore prevented him from seeing what the condition of the centre of the bridge was, but very shortly after that, as he continued to look at the bridge, he noticed that a portion of it was down. He then went to an upper window to look at the bridge. The direction from which the wind was coming was a direction that he knew quite clearly would test the bridge as severely as any other could. In the years he had been observing the weather he had never known any such wind before. There had been storms before approaching that night's storm in velocity, but not in force or that sort of swirly nature, like a whirlwind.

McKelvie could not account for having had on previous occasions wind of the same velocity and character yet with less pressure than on the night of the 28th. The testing of the pressure was merely a matter of opinion – he had no instrument to test the opinion that he had formed.

In Dundee there were a great many large chimney stacks, and some were in such a position as to be affected with considerable force by wind coming from the south-west and hauling round to the west, many of them ranging from below Lochee downwards on the coast. To McKelvie's knowledge none of those chimney stacks came down that night, but he could not account for the fact that, if the force of the wind had brought down the bridge, why it had not brought down some of the chimneys.

Although none of the large chimneys were blown down, the effect of the night's storm on the Balgay Cemetery was that eight monuments were blown down completely and one partly. In the eastern cemetery 13 were blown down; these had been standing perhaps seven or eight feet above the ground. Some were also blown down on the north slope, facing the river. None were blown down on the south-west slope, or on the summit. The eastern cemetery was rather sideways to the gale: it sloped from north to south, and the gale came from west to east. It would, therefore, be exposed to the wind hauling round from south-west to west. In none of the previous gales had there been a similar disaster in the cemeteries.

Charles Clark was a retired businessman who had lived in Dundee for 52 years. He had kept a record of the weather in his home on Magdalen Green as a matter of private amusement and information for some 14 years, and twice a day his record showed the readings of the barometer and the thermometer. Clark also had his own way of recording the force of the wind, although he had no instrument for testing wind pressure.

At 9 o'clock in the morning and 9 o'clock in the evening on 28 December Clark had recorded the weather in his usual way. His barometer recorded at 9 o'clock in the morning a pressure reading of 29.20psi. His house was some 50 feet above sea level. That evening the barometer reading was 29.60psi when he came home from church. He later looked at his barometer and it was then the same as in the morning.

The lowest reading for wind speed that Clark observed was at tea-time, about 5 o'clock; his scale measured from 0 to 6, and he recorded the wind that night at 4. It had never reached 5 on his scale, so this was about the heaviest storm he had ever encountered. He thought that perhaps two or three times in the previous 14 years he had seen that level of wind equalled, but never exceeded.

Further accounts of the weather conditions came from men connected with the Royal Navy training ship *Mars*, which was stationed in the Tay on the night the bridge went down. The ship had been built of oak as a man-of-war at Chatham in the 1840s and had arrived on the Tay in 1869. The gunnery instructor on board the *Mars* was Edward Batsworth, who had first gone to sea in the Navy in 1853. He was on watch, but not deck watch, for a great part of that night, beginning at 5 o'clock up until about 9.

When Batsworth went on duty the weather came to blow very hard by degrees, but it was not so strong at 5 o'clock as from 7 to 8. Even at 5 o'clock it was blowing pretty stiffly, in a continuous gale and was coming down in squalls at intervals. Therefore he thought the weather was a continuous gale with the addition of periodic squalls or gusts.

Batsworth had been stationed on the Tay for just under two and a half years, and during that time had never experienced wind of that violence. His log showed that the wind that night at 12 o'clock was blowing from 4 to 8 – the Navy scale for recording wind was gradated to 12, and Batsworth thought it reached 11 later that night. That was an exceptionally high wind for a northern climate.

Hugh McMahon was a seaman instructor on board the *Mars*. He had a long record of sailing in the Merchant Navy, in which he had been a boatswain and able seaman. He had worked on the ship for almost three years. On 28 December he was on deck in the watch from 4 o'clock until 8. It was his duty to make observations every hour.

The wind that night was stronger than he had ever recorded before, a very strong gale. There were also gusts or squalls coming down very hard indeed, which made a great noise. The ship that afternoon was specially lashed to prevent danger of loss or being washed away. McMahon acted under the orders of Captain Scott in making things all secure.

John Jack was 86 years old, and as a younger man he had been in command of a merchant ship for 22 years. His ships had generally traded between the Canary Islands and London, and Russia, Prussia and up the Baltic Sea. Then he had become dock and harbour-master at Dundee for 36 years, retiring from that position six years before the bridge went down. Jack lived at Tayport, 2 miles from the River Tay.

Although he never went outdoors during the storm, he had a fine view of the river from upstairs and he was there most of the time. The river was running very high: it was a sheet of foam and there was a great deal of spray thrown about. The moon was bright at times, and at other times it was so dark that one could see nothing. Jack had never seen such a very loud storm of wind before. Every five or ten minutes there would be a gust; the gale was heavy, but when a gust came it was such as he had never heard before. Jack thought it was like artillery going off.

Jack was afraid to go out to see how his house was coping with the storm. The next day a member of the family was visiting between 11 and 12 o'clock, and when he came he related that he had come across a piece of lead about 13 feet long and a foot broad that had been blown off Jack's roof. Jack's impression was strongly that had the wind continued for half an hour longer there would not have remained any of the roof on his house: the eaves were beginning to open up.

His concerns and those of other weather-watchers in the Tay Estuary were certainly well-founded, and were confirmed by no less an authority than the Astronomer Royal, who, in the days before weather forecasts on radio and television, was regarded as the best authority on weather in Great Britain. Sir G. B. Airey told the Court of Inquiry that he had observed that the shape of the Tay Valley made structures in it particularly at risk from adverse weather conditions, certainly compared to, for example, the estuary of the Forth.

8
THE LAST TRAIN SUCCESSFULLY TO CROSS THE TAY BRIDGE

*'The driver did not feel the bridge
oscillate or vibrate more than usual.'*

The last train successfully to cross the Tay Bridge before it went down on Sunday 28 December was the 5.50pm passenger train from Tayport to Dundee. It was driven by Alexander Kennedy, who had been a driver on the northern section of the North British Railway for six years, between Dundee and Burntisland. The train's route was from Burntisland via Cupar and Tayport.

Kennedy's train consisted of five carriages and two brake-vans. It got to the Tay Bridge at 6.03pm and crossed the bridge in safety. There was nothing unusual about the passage that evening. Kennedy did not in the least feel the train vibrate or the bridge oscillate more than usual. The wind was blowing a strong gale, though he had crossed over the bridge in storms of similar strength before. Everything about the bridge seemed in good order; although Kennedy did notice that the guard put the brake on as the train came towards the north end of the bridge, where the incline was. Brakes were fitted to the engine and the guard's van, and there was a further brake on the last van.

The driver did not notice whether putting on the brake caused any sparks to come from the wheels of his train or engine. Kennedy had on previous journeys across the bridge seen sparks emitted from the wheels by application of the brake: this was a common thing. The brake would only be put on after the train had reached the top of the incline, as it went down towards the north.

That Sunday night, 28 December, Kennedy did not see any sparks. He did not presume that because he had not seen any that there were none – he was standing on the westward side of the engine cab facing into the wind. He emphasised that there was nothing peculiar about seeing sparks. He felt perfectly sure there was no uneasy movement in his engine as it crossed the bridge.

In conclusion, Kennedy thought that everything about the bridge and his train that night had been in perfectly good order. During his years as an engine driver he had never known a passenger carriage to be blown over by the wind.

Robert Shand was Kennedy's guard that night. Like Kennedy, he noticed that the wind was blowing very hard, but unlike Kennedy, who recalled storms of similar strength in the past, Shand could scarcely recall it ever having blown so hard on any other occasion when he had been crossing the bridge. But like Kennedy, he did not feel any unusual oscillation while crossing.

However, before the train came to the south end of the high girders, he, unlike Kennedy, did notice some sparks. These were coming from the wheel of a carriage in the train, the third carriage towards the rear of the train in front of the 3rd Class carriage. Before seeing the sparks Shand had not put on the brakes; but seeing them he immediately put on his brake, before the train reached the top of the incline. This action had no effect upon the sparks – they still continued. Indeed, they then also began to come from the brake-van, and continued from the composite carriage in front until the train reached the curve on the north end. Shand took off the brake when the train was at about the middle of the high girders, just about the time when it began to descend the incline.

Kennedy's train was then running downhill and Shand would not always put on his brake when the train reached that point – it would depend on its speed. If a train was running at the regulation speed upon the bridge he would not normally apply his brake at that point, so Shand released the brake in the high girders, because he was certain there was nothing wrong with the train then. Nor could he see anything out of order with the bridge that night.

At first, Shand thought the sparks were the result of an axle having broken. He therefore put on the brake to stop the train until it was found out whether that was so or not. Shand also hung out a red lamp from the side of his van, but Kennedy did not see it and it was not answered or responded to in any way. Shand's next thought was that the sparks were being caused by the wind, which, he thought, was forcing the wheels of the carriages against the rail.

The sparks did not continue until the train reached the north cabin, but had ceased by the time the train got to the Distant signal. While Shand was thinking that the axle was broken, he felt concerned for the train's safety as it crossed the Tay Bridge, but not afterwards – he had been worried about the axle breaking on the bridge. Apart from that, Shand apprehended no danger to himself or to the train from the condition of the bridge or the state of the weather. He had never apprehended danger in crossing that bridge, and had never given anyone reason to suppose that he apprehended danger.

At the Distant signal the bridge curved to the east, and in Shand's opinion the stress would be then taken off the wheels and they would not be pressed against the rail. The sparks ceased then. When the train arrived at Dundee Shand examined the wheels of the carriage from which the sparks had been emitted, but saw nothing at all that might have led him to suppose that anything was wrong. He had been looking out of the eastward side of his van when he saw the sparks, the right-hand side of the train as it approached Dundee. He had never before seen sparks in the straight of the bridge, although he had seen them before from the brakes in running round a curve.

The Court of Inquiry also heard evidence from some of the passengers on that last train successfully to cross the Tay Bridge. John Buick, who lived at Dundee, was a fitter in the engine shop of the Caledonian Railway, and on the night of the disaster he left Tayport for Dundee on the 5.50 train, travelling in the guard's van.

Buick travelled in the train from Tayport, stopping at Newport on its way to Dundee. At the bridge the train was travelling at around 3 or 4mph to allow the baton to be picked up. Buick did not know at what time this happened, so could not say when his train reached the south cabin of the Tay Bridge.

The night was very stormy and after the baton had been collected Buick noticed that fire was coming from the wheels, appearing as if a brake had been put on. He described the fire as 'following flashes', coming from about the centre of the train, further forward than the carriage next to him. The fire appeared to him to be coming from just one carriage, about the centre of the train.

Buick was sitting in the front of the van looking through a small projecting window that enabled him to look forward along the side of the train. He told the guard, Shand, that there was something up with the train, and he should look out. Shand went and looked out, and replied that the train was hard running against the check-rail (an additional rail or rails provided inside the running rails to keep the wheel flanges running true, as on a sharp curve or bridge). They looked again and it appeared to be getting worse, so Shand put on the brake, giving it a good twist. The speed of the train slackened a little, but less than one would have expected given that Shand had given the brake such a good twist. Buick thought nobody in the train would have noticed the speed diminishing as a result of Shand's action.

Buick thought the diminution in the speed was so small that the driver might well not have noticed that the brake had been applied. Despite this limited effect, he perceived that the train did steady a little, but there was no other effect produced by the tightening of the brake. The guard also put out the red lamp over the door on the east side. The application of the brake did make the flashes a good deal less frequent, but they continued the whole way across the bridge to a reduced degree. Buick could not say how long Shand kept the brake on; he was too busy observing the movement of the train. He was a little afraid, initially worried that an axle might have broken. The carriage was bearing upon the west side with the wind. Buick did not look out on the other side of the train.

Buick was not sure if the carriage was tilted up or not, but could only feel that it was just sort of moving, shaking from top to bottom. It was canting rather to the east, although he was not sure exactly by how much. He felt that this was a result of the wind's action on the train, but not, he felt, the wind's action on the bridge – he thought the bridge was right enough. The up and down motion had started about half-way through the high girders, before the brake had been put on at all; the brake lessened and steadied the motion a little, but did not stop it. The driver paid no attention to the putting on of the brake or the showing of the lamp; he neither stopped the train nor sounded his whistle.

Buick thought the train ran across the bridge at somewhere between 14 and 20mph with the brake on. However, the brake really made very little difference. He did not see the fire all the way to the north side – it stopped when the train got to the curve. While Buick had felt the carriage rolling up and down, he did not feel much side-to-side motion; he thought there was nothing unusual in the motion of the train from side to side.

On arrival at Dundee station Buick saw the guard and another man going along the train examining the wheels to see if they were all right – their examination showed that they were. Buick told nobody that he had seen the fire, which, he concluded, must have been caused by the wind pressing the carriage over on the check-rail, or guard-rail, thus producing sparks that were being blown under the carriage by the wind from west to east. The fire was coming from, he thought, the rails, although he could not assert this confidently. His first impression was that there was something wrong with the axle, although that proved not to be the case – he then formed the view that the wind was to blame. The fire ceased when the train got so far north as to be out of the direct blast of the wind.

The effect of putting on the brake had been to diminish the sparks and to tighten down the train at the tail end. The heavy engine at the front, thought Buick, held down the front of the train all right, so that the train would be tightened down to the rail. Therefore it would be less loose at the tail than it was before the brake was put on, which was, Buick thought, quite consistent with his views as to the effect of the wind.

Buick was quite satisfied that there was nothing wrong with the bridge. He knew a little about bridges, and a great deal about engines. The effect of putting the brake on had been very limited, and the engine driver, instead of stopping, had put on more steam, with the result that there was only a little stoppage of the speed.

Buick had first observed the sparks when the train was half-way between the south cabin and the high girders. Immediately afterwards the brake had been put on, but Buick did not notice the guard taking off the brake, and only noticed that it had been done while passing through the high girders. By then the sparks were not as bad as they had been at first, but as the train got between the girders they kept sparking away.

John Black was 21 and worked in the Parcels Office of the Caledonian Railway at Dundee. On 28 December he came from the south side of the Tay to the north on the 5.50pm from Tayport to Dundee. He did not know the name of the driver, but travelled in the guard's van with another man named Buick and the guard, Shand. Black, like Buick, was in the guard's van because he had arrived too late to look for accommodation in the train, and he knew the guard – indeed, having done the crossing several times, he thought he knew most of the guards by sight.

Black said that the night was extremely stormy, and the train was only travelling at 3 to 4mph when it reached the south cabin of the Tay Bridge, a very moderate speed. It picked up speed after the baton had been collected, then Buick told Black of fire flying from the wheels of the train. Buick was standing looking out of the train at the time, at one of the little windows at the front of the van that enabled him to see forward, and he called attention to the flames.

Black looked out and saw numerous sparks on the east side of the train, coming from the rear carriage, the carriage next to the van, but immediately afterwards he noticed them from the whole of the carriages, spreading all along the train. The guard also looked at the sparks, then put on his brakes and held his red lamp out at the window.

Black thought the driver did nothing to indicate that he was responding to the use of the brake by bringing up the train. So far as he could see, the driver disregarded the putting on of the brake and certainly gave no answer to the signal-lamp.

The wind was blowing from the west. When the train slowed in response to the brake, Black could see that the sparks continued to proceed from the whole train, though to a lesser degree. After the guard loosened his brake again, and the train went on, Black noticed that the sparks were fewer in number than they had been when the brake was applied. The sparks were worse when Black first noticed them, but when the train went on, with the brake eased again, the sparks did not increase, but kept decreasing.

When Black looked out on the west side he felt motion in the van – a violent swaying from side to side – but felt no other motion at all. When gusts of wind came, they perceptibly affected the carriage, seeming somehow to tilt it over eastwards. Black could not say whether it was the wind affecting the bridge, and the bridge tilting the van over, or whether it was the wind upon the van that tilted it over. He saw no wheels leave the rail. The sparks appeared to have been caused by the wheel pressing upon the rail, by the friction between the two. Black did not feel the bridge moving at that time, although he did feel the motion in the carriage; he did not know whether there was a corresponding motion at the time upon the bridge.

Everything that Black felt and saw on that occasion was consistent with his view that the wind was bearing against the carriages and pressing them against the rail. He did not attribute it to any shaking in the bridge, or the blowing over of the bridge, as distinguished from the train. When the brake was applied the carriages ceased to bear over as much as they had done when they were going at a greater speed. Black only saw the carriages tilting over when he looked out on the west side – he did not feel it, only saw it. It was just as if the wind was slightly bearing them out of their perpendicular a little, which would be quite consistent with the sparks coming from the east side and falling against the rail.

When Black saw the sparks diminish that did not show him that the carriages were bearing less against the rail – the lessened speed of the train would account for that. Black felt sure that the carriages had not given way more than the springs would allow, and he did not think that the bridge was out of perpendicular. He had looked out of the carriage window in going round the curve and had seen the train bearing slightly over, but this he attributed solely to the action of the wind upon the carriage.

Reverend George Grubb was an Episcopalian clergyman, one of the clergy of St Paul's in Dundee. On the night of the bridge's fall he took the 5.50pm train from Newport to Dundee, a route he travelled very frequently, including journeys when the wind was pretty high. Grubb travelled 1st Class.

On the night of 28 December Grubb was surprised that the train did not suffer greater effects from the wind when crossing the bridge. The wind was higher than he had ever experienced before, so he expected to feel it more than previously.

After the train entered the south end of the bridge, one of his fellow passengers opened a window facing west. This was in the course of a conversation between them, when Grubb remarked upon the curious effects that were sometimes felt when crossing the bridge in a high wind. The other passenger therefore decided to try the effects by opening the window, which produced an effect somewhat similar to shocks of electricity felt in the ears, first one ear, then the other. This effect was most marked when crossing the high girders, where there was latticework between Grubb and the wind. The open window was to the windward – Grubb did not open the window on the other side of the carriage.

Grubb did not feel the slightest movement or oscillation on crossing the bridge, nor did he feel any movement, vibration or oscillation, in the carriage that he could attribute to the strong wind. He observed the state of the river while the train was passing over it, finding it very rough. There was foam flying about, and the wind seemed to be very high beneath the bridge. The train arrived at Dundee at exactly a quarter past six by the clock in the station.

9

THE CONDITION OF THE WRECKAGE

The wrecked bridge

'On that first dip he found the columns that were there, all lying about in one confused mass, everything all broken.'

The best accounts of the condition in which the bridge had been left following its fall came from some of the divers who were sent down to inspect it. The following accounts give some sense of the developing knowledge of the condition of the bridge as successive divers reported what they had found.

The methodology of the diving operations was set out to the Court of Inquiry by William Robertson, who, as harbour-master of Dundee, had overall charge of the operations. As we have already seen, he also gave evidence as a frequent passenger over the Tay Bridge line, and as someone who had made frequent observations of the time trains were taking to cross the bridge.

In his capacity as superintendent of the diving operations, Robertson arranged to have divers ready to inspect the wreckage of both the bridge and the train. He himself went out a good deal with the divers, directing the places at which the barges were to be moored, and the places where the men were to go down. Robertson saw everything recovered by the divers.

One of the first divers to go down, on Monday 29 December, was John Cocks. He lived in Dundee, and was employed by Robertson to go to the scene of the wreck of the bridge. He first went down on the Monday morning, the day after the fall of the bridge, completing one dive, or dip, that day, some 30 feet south of No 3 pier (the third broken pier counting from the south). Cocks found some girders lying on their sides. He travelled in both directions and found more girders both north and south of where he had gone down, but found none of them broken. Cocks found nothing else that day.

The first trace of the train was found on the Wednesday afternoon, 31 December, three days after the bridge had gone down. One of the divers working for the harbour trustees came up and said, when he got on the barge, 'We have got something now.' The diver pointed to his line and Robertson's men hauled upon it. Robertson was afraid that the men would break the line, so told them to stop. As the tide had commenced to run pretty strongly, Robertson told the diver to go down and cut a piece off whatever it was. The diver said it was something like tarpaulin or cloth.

The diver thought it was a carriage he had found. He went down again, and when he came up there was, fast to the line, a piece of lining with hair stuffing from a 1st Class carriage. The diver had also brought up a piece of waxed floor cloth. It was not possible for the divers to go down again that day, and Robertson and his men went away home with a melancholy satisfaction that they had at least found a trace of the train.

Robertson's men had made fast a rope to the spot where the man had cut this stuff out, and when they went back the next day Robertson sent a diver down by this line. When he came up he told them that he had been into the 1st Class carriage, but there was nothing in it.

Having heard Captain Robertson's overall view of the diving operations, the Court of Inquiry then heard from various individual divers on their work at the scene and on what they had discovered about the wreck of both the bridge and the train itself.

Robertson sent Edward Simpson down after Cocks, and he reported to Robertson that he had gone into a 3rd Class carriage. He then went down again and reported to the harbour-master, 'I have been into another 3rd Class carriage.' When Simpson went down yet again he reported, 'I have been now on the engine.'

On Tuesday 30th John Cocks made two dips, one in the forenoon, the other in the afternoon. He went down near No 3 pier, but to the north of it, and travelled from there northwards to No 4 pier.

The same day Peter Harley made his first dip. He lived at Tayport, and had been a diver for 14 or 15 years. He dived at the Tay Bridge on William Robertson's instructions. When he went down he landed in the bed of the river about abreast of No 3 pier. He then went about 6 or 8 yards towards the bridge, but found nothing.

On Wednesday 31 December John Cocks dived again, in the forenoon. In the afternoon he went down to between 20 and 30 feet north of No 4 pier, where he found a girder and the 1st Class carriage. There was also another girder there, lying on its side, in the same line as the girder he had previously found. Cocks did not find any part of the girders broken to the northwards of the pier.

When Cocks found his first trace of the train, the 1st Class carriage, he was unable to examine it because the tide was too strong and his time was up. On a later dip he went through the carriage and examined it thoroughly to see if anything was in it. It was wrecked: the roof was completely off and the windows and doors were broken. He found just one door, the southernmost one, swinging on its hinges – it had not been shattered at all. As it was a 1st Class carriage there were three doorways and three windows in all, but only that one door remained. He found only some cushions and some broken pieces of wood; he brought some of the cushions up and some of the oil-cloth from the floor of the carriage. The oil-cloth was hanging out of the carriage, jammed between the carriage and the top part of the girder. Cocks made a second dip on that Wednesday, when he went to the south of No 4 pier; working his way southwards, he found nothing south of No 4 but the girders.

On the same day Peter Norley made several dips. On the first he found the bridge and its girders, then he went down again, by the 1st Class carriage, which was about abreast of No 4 pier. He did not go through the carriage on this occasion, but later that day he did try to get access to it, but found that he could not do so safely. Norley tried to break it up, to tear some portions of it away.

John Barclay was a diver who lived in North Shields. He had had a good deal of experience of diving, some seven years in all. He went to the Tay Bridge because he needed work, and got it from Dugald Drummond, the North British Railway's Locomotive Superintendent. He began work on Thursday 1 January, and went down several times, each dip at pretty much the same place, where there was a girder, between the third and fourth piers, counting from the south. When he got down he inspected over a distance of some 50 feet, finding that the girder was entire, not broken. He found nothing else that day.

Captain Robertson was at the site of the diving operations again on Thursday 1st and the next two days. Some warming foot-pans and some lamps were found on the Thursday, then on the next day, when Robertson's men started out again, it came on to blow a gale before they could get to the spot, and they could not stay out. On Saturday 3 January they had a good day; but they did not get very much, only some lamps – the men supposed that the remainder of the train was cut all to pieces.

When John Cocks went down once more, on 1 January, he went into the 1st Class carriage to examine it more thoroughly. He was able to form a view of the condition in which the wreck of the bridge had left the carriage: he found that the windows and all but one door were gone and the roof was completely off, although the floor was whole. The carriage was standing upright, on its wheels. Cocks did not find the north end of the carriage, but at the south end the compartments were all intact. Cocks could find nothing but the shell of the carriage – the inside had been completely shattered. There was nothing, only the cushioning and padding, all the way through it.

One of the carriages that Cocks found on another dip was lying hard upon the east side of the top part of the girder, inside it. He did not find anything broken.

On Thursday 1 January Peter Harley could not go down, nor on the Friday. On the Saturday he went down at the 1st Class carriage and thoroughly searched the two compartments of the carriage he had found before. Harley found the inside fittings, but did not find any bodies, and no luggage – nothing except what belonged to the carriage.

On Friday 2 January John Cocks was not down – it was too stormy – but he did two dips on the Saturday, between Nos 3 and 4 piers. He worked his way to the eastward of the girder, along the bed of the river, but found nothing – no trace of any carriage or brake-van. On his second dip he went down between 20 and 30 feet from No 4 pier, and made his way northwards. He found a girder broken there, at the place where he had descended. He was at the bottom boom of the girder as it was lying. The top boom was standing – the right-hand or upper boom when the girder was up, on the east side. This was the only part of that girder he came across. He also found a roof lamp within the girder, just at the break. The water in which he found the lamp was very thick and muddy – he could not see much in it and had to ascertain most things by touch.

The fractured end of the girder that Cocks had found was resting upon another, not upon the bed of the river – resting on the latticework, the cross-work of the girder when it had been standing. The facing of the girder was about 3 feet clear of the bed of the river.

The same day Cocks went down to the south side of pier No 4 to look for the rear part of the train. South of that pier he found nothing but a girder and some eight or nine roof-lamps about 50 feet to the east of the girders. They were scattered – he found some inside the girders and some outside. He did not find any trace of a carriage or a van there, although there were some of the door head-railings belonging to a 3rd Class carriage. Cocks found no trace of any van or carriage to the south of the 1st Class carriage that he had previously found.

William Norley was 2nd captain of the main top, seaman gunner, torpedo man and a diver on board the gunboat *Lord Warden*. His captain instructed him to dive at the scene of the wreck of the bridge, and he first went down on Saturday 3 January. He went down three times that day, between the third and fourth piers, the broken piers, to the east of the girder. When he got down he proceeded in a circle for about 10 or 12 feet until he came upon a girder, which was broken. Norley felt it with his hands, the part of the girder nearest the bed of the river, in the sand. When he came to one end of the girder he found that it was broken, but the other bit of it he did not trace. There was a sandbank there, and he felt something in the gravel or sand. He could not make out what it was at first, but it was revealed as a wide plank. He hardly knew what he was diving for other than parts of carriages and bodies. He came up and reported his finds and the sandbank.

Norley then took a line down with him, and tried to find the plank of wood again. He went over the bank and round it, but could find no trace of it. The tide was then running rather strongly. He made a third dip that day. The barge from which he had been diving had been shifted more towards the third pier, further south. He went down there, but found nothing except a continuation of the girder.

John Barclay also went down several times, the first time somewhere abreast of pier No 4. He found the girder as he had previously done, which was lying pretty much in a continuous line from north to south. He also got hold of a broken lamp inside the girder. That was all he found to the east of the piers.

Later that Saturday Barclay was let down to the west of the piers, close to No 4. There he found a coupling of a carriage underneath the bridge. The west part of the bridge was lying at an angle of 45 degrees and Barclay had to get underneath it to fetch out the coupling, but the flood tide was too strong, and he knocked off from that part of the job. The coupling had been lying on the clear sand, with the bent girder round about it, and in places sand was silting up. The coupling was not entire, but was broken at the end that had gone into the carriage.

The next day, Sunday 4 January, the divers did not start at the same point where they had left off, but at the southernmost pier. They went from that pier further to the south, where the bridge was standing. Captain

Robertson's men had therefore by now examined from the engine at the front of the train to where the bridge was still standing – they had gone over the whole space in which any part of the train could have been.

William Norley went down again on that Sunday, making another three dips. On his first he went down to the north of that part of the wreck that showed at low water, the girder. When he got down he travelled west, up the river, then north, then south, but he could not go too far underneath on account of the broken parts of the bridge; the latticework was jagged, and it fouled his pipe. He intended to go through the top of the girder, but Robertson said that he was to go further over. Norley found the columns that were there all lying about in one confused mass, everything broken. The latticework was all jagged and broken too, some of it above his head.

On his second dip that day Peter Norley worked further towards the south, between the first and second piers. He did find some broken parts of the girder but the main part of it was whole. Norley went through two parts, as it was on its side. However, part of what he had found lying on the ground below, which came up to about his middle from the sand, was broken. Norley sent up a piece of hand-rail he found – he knew it was part of the bridge because it was painted light blue.

On his third dip that Sunday Norley went down nearly against the main structure of the bridge, the last standing pillar. He went down through the girders again there, right down between the lattices, the diagonal stays, right in the centre of the girder. He found that it was more solid, not so confined as it was further to the north, and much less twisted or crushed. However, he found nothing to send up from there.

John Barclay also went down again several times on that Sunday, as often as the tide and the weather permitted. He went down to the east side of the girders, a little to the north of where he had previously gone down, and found a 1st Class carriage lying hard against the girders. It was standing on its bottom, on its wheels. Barclay smashed one of the doors, the only entire one left, and went in. The roof of the carriage was off, as was the south end of the vehicle, and the internal compartments were all in a wreck together. Barclay fetched some floor cloth out from the carriage, but nothing else. Only part of the floor of the carriage was entire – the south end had given way, but the flooring was there.

Barclay was then told to start diving north of the 1st Class carriage. He went down between the girders, and thought he put his hand into the funnel of the engine, but the tide was too strong, and he found himself in a confused mess trying to get out. The state of the tide prevented him making any further examination, and he had to come up.

The last day of the diving operations was Monday 5 January. That day Robertson's men found, about 40 feet from the 1st Class carriage, the tail-lamp that should have been fast to the guard's van at the end of the train. They also found, a little further north, three carriage-lamps that had been fastened to the roof of the carriage. One diver found a 2nd Class lamp, on the southern part, and another diver brought up two 3rd Class lamps from a little further north.

Peter Harley went down on that Monday, at about No 5 pier, where he came upon a broken girder; this he detected by going along it with his hand. He came to the end of it, and found where it was broken, feeling the break all around. Then he went to the other bit of it, which he found some 20 or 30 feet from the first split he had earlier found. The space between the two ends of the broken bit was about as much as he could get his hand in. There might have been more, but that was how he tested it was broken, by feeling with his hand.

Harley went down a second time and cleared away the wreckage further south of where he had been diving earlier, but he found nothing, and the pressure of the tide was pushing him away from the carriage.

William Norley also went down that day, between the fourth and fifth piers to the east of the girder, which he found by making a circle. He found that the girder was to the west of where he had gone down, and was solid right along; he travelled a good 10 feet along it to ascertain its condition. He found some parts of the telegraph wire insulators, although there was no wire on them any more. There was also a piece of lead, the sole of a diver's boot or something. He found nothing belonging to the train or the bridge.

On his second dip Norley went down in the same place, made for the girder again and went north about 10 or 15 feet. He climbed up the girder and got in through the angle-iron and worked along inside until he came to a part of the carriage. It seemed to be the 1st Class carriage; there were cushions all around, and a kind of network at one end, a rod and network inside it. In it he found two foot-warming pans. Some of the roof and sides were gone. The carriage was standing nearly fair, leaning rather towards the west. It was upright, but not on its wheels. While part of the roof was off, the rear part of the carriage was nearly whole. After examining the carriage Norley went up, then, when he went down again, he found part of the buffers of the carriage.

Norley had found the columns all broken up and in a heap. They were in a regular confusion, as if something had thrown them over and they were scattered, like a lot of bricks fallen down. Norley stood on the bottom where the other girder was breast high, and found that there were irons underneath. That part seemed to be fair, just as if it had been on the pier, and the other part seemed as if it had been turned over, capsized.

On that Monday morning, 5 January, John Barclay went down again several times. In the morning he went down to the east side of where he had found the broken bridge the day before, to the south of No 4 pier. He had been ordered to go down to look at the girders, to see if he could find the break. He found it in the bottom of the girder and got at it by going down on his rope and going along the bottom of the girder until he came to it, on the ground. The break was found some 25 or 26 feet south of No 4 pier, but in the murky conditions he could see nothing of the break, relying on touch.

The girder where Barclay found the break was a terrible ragged mass. There was a distinct break and a displacement of the line at the boom of the girder. What he found broken was the bottom of the top of the bridge, or what had been the top of the bridge when it had been still standing. When he saw it, it was on the ground, on the lowest of the girders.

After Barclay had found this break he was ordered to examine the river. He went down the river some 100 yards from the bridge, his orders being to look for bodies, but he found none, only a piece of a 3rd Class carriage from its side and a portion of the iron. He also found a lamp.

The divers worked with a strong ebb tide, then a pretty strong flood tide, for two and a half hours a day, which was about the maximum that a man could work in those conditions. Robertson did not like to put a man among such debris as that in a tideway at night time, so the men only worked in daylight.

The men found the engine lying a little south of the fifth broken pier, on the eastern side of the bridge; at most it was some 40 or 50 feet from the bridge, east of the piers, immediately south of the fifth pier. The lamps his men had found were just outside of the fallen girders, where the girders had tumbled down on the east side, and the engine was found inside the girders.

Robertson did not know anything about the whereabouts of the tender, and did not know if it had become separated from the engine. He intended to make a thorough examination of the engine, but after his men got there Robertson thought it was still more important to persevere and try to find the remains of the missing carriages. The day Robertson was giving evidence to the Court of Inquiry he had a diver working on the wreck of the train, and obviously did not have the results of that man's work.

The stream of the tide would run down an hour after low water; indeed, with certain winds it would continue to run down for an hour. Robertson referred to a visible girder, which was the top of the lower girder lying broadside. The furthest east portion of it was all above the ground at about a man's height; it seemed to be lying on its edge, with a slight cant to the westward. It was not resting upon gravel or stones – the divers could get right underneath it.

John Robertson was engaged in the operations of lifting the fallen remains of the Tay Bridge. He was not related to William Robertson. During this work he found a strut with marks upon it – it had been struck at the south side. The angle-iron and covering-plate were all turned up and burst in three or four places, and the web of the strut was all broken. The girder to which the strut belonged was broken into many different pieces, but Robertson could hardly say how many.

He looked at the wrought-iron tie-bars that were bolted to the permanent way beams, one every 18 feet or so; these had been added in order to keep the gauge accurate, at the suggestion of General Hutchinson, the Board of Trade inspector of railways who had given the Tay Bridge its certificate to be opened for the carriage of passengers. They were bars of flat iron, about 6 inches by half an inch, and Robertson found marks on some of them, which he thought indicated that the carriages in front of the van had left the rails. Robertson produced some of the bars for the Court of Inquiry to examine, and it certainly appeared as if the wheels of a carriage had been on them.

Robertson said that the bars had been found in the fifth girder. The fourth girder, between piers Nos 3 and 4, was in several pieces, and part of it was broken up at the end; they had made an attempt to cut it and lift it with dynamite. The marks were one on the upper side and two underneath the boom. Therefore Robertson thought that a flange had struck it, that the flange of a wheel had got underneath the boom. He thought the wheel was off the rail and would have slid off underneath and smashed through the planking. It was bound to have gone underneath because this was on top of the way-beams.

Robertson had worked on the railway for a good many years, and in that time he had seen cases where the rear carriage of a train had gone off the line. The effect that had upon the carriage immediately in front could be to throw it off too, and the effect on the rails would be to mark the chairs and occasionally the rails too. It might also have the effect of tearing up the rails.

Robertson believed that if there had been a violent action that had thrown a carriage off the rails, he would have expected to find, naturally, some mark upon the rails. A carriage was bound to go off on the same level as the carriage in front of it, then the buffer would go under the one in front and would have a tendency to throw it off. Robertson had seen cases before when the fore-carriage had been thrown off in that way. The carriages would always fall over to the outside. A carriage would not be so easily lifted out where there was a guard-rail, but if it had been raised up outside of the guard-rail, it would have gone.

The last diver to give evidence to the Court of Inquiry was Henry Dewey, who was engaged in assisting to raise the wrecked girders of the Tay Bridge. He made his first dip on 6 April 1880, and the Court of Inquiry's report was to be published on 8 May. Dewey dived near where the 2nd Class carriage was and came down in the middle of that carriage. He worked to the southward until he came to the buffers of another carriage. He tried to ascertain whether they were attached or not – that was his first object, to see if they were clear. He found that they were disconnected, that the couplings were broken.

Dewey then came up to report to Thomas Armit, who was superintending the raising of the fallen portions of the Tay Bridge. He told Armit that one carriage was on top of the other. Dewey proceeded to make slings fast to the 2nd Class carriage; he planned to take the south end first, and Armit had got his line ready to take that end. He and Armit later went down together and slung the 2nd Class carriage, putting the chains on. Afterwards Dewey went down again with the line that he had fastened, and lifted the van.

Dewey never touched the girder underneath the carriages. When he got to the sole-plate at the south end of the 2nd Class carriage, he found the buffers of another carriage above his head; at that time he was crawling along on the beams, the water was dark and he could not see very well at all. However, he felt the buffer, and thought that it had overlapped the 2nd Class carriage sole-plate by about 4 feet, as near as he could judge, for he did not stop any great time there. As soon as he came to the buffer, his first object was to put his hand across to see that the couplings were clear.

Dewey found no difficulty at all in raising the 2nd Class carriage. It came up quite easily, and hardly shook the other one as it came up. Then the other one was resting on its end; when the men went to put a sling round it for the purpose of raising it, to stand it on its bottom, it was just as much as they could do to reeve the chain round.

Dewey thought that the underside of the buffer was about 2½ feet above the sole-plate of the 2nd Class carriage that he was crawling along. He could have got under it by putting his hand under it, but he did not want to do so because he had the coupling of the carriage above him and his pipes were attached to his helmet, making it impossible to do so safely. He did not come to any wheels; he came down on the top of the carriage, and saw no wheels attached at all. He came down to the wood of the 2nd Class carriage, but still saw no wheels.

The Members of the Joint Committee of the Tay Bridge Undertaking and the Chairman and Directors of the North British Railway request the favor of Mr James Bell Junr's Company on the occasion of the opening of the Tay Bridge and Railways, at Dundee on Friday the 31st Current

Edinburgh,
27th May, 1878.

Secretary

An early answer will oblige.

For Train arrangements see other side.

Above An invitation to James Bell, Jnr, to attend the opening of the Tay Bridge and associated railways at Dundee on 31 May 1878; there is a programme of events on the back of the card. *National Archives of Scotland*

Fancy might try, in vain, to paint upon the page of thought, Thy image; for thy mighty form with loftiest grace is fraught,

Each charm, which from our ken was hid in unseen worlds concealed, Here, gathered in thy perfect self is to our eyes revealed.–

Right An illustration from the menu card for the opening of the Forth Bridge, showing both the Forth and Tay Bridges. *National Archives of Scotland*

The bridge under construction: a 31-foot-diameter caisson on its barge, ready to be towed out to construct the foundation for a pier. *Dundee Central Library*

Above A view of the bridge being built in 1878, seen from the north bank. *University of St Andrews*

Below The bridge under construction, looking this time from Fife towards Dundee. *University of St Andrews*

Above Men at work at the south end of the bridge. *Dundee Central Library*

Below The completed bridge. The new signal box at the junction has been provided for the opening of the Tayport line in May 1879, which is seen coming in from the right. The original line to St Fort and Edinburgh is in the left foreground. It is at this new cabin that the driver of the doomed train would collect the single-line baton. *University of St Andrews*

A steam locomotive on the newly completed bridge in 1878, showing clearly the single line through the high girders. *University of St Andrews*

The full sweep of the Tay Bridge seen both before and after the disaster.
University of St Andrews

Ex-Provost William Robertson, the Dundee harbour-master
and eye-witness. *Dundee Central Library*

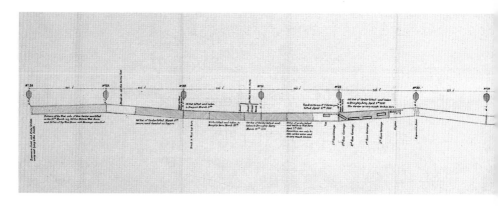

Above This diagram from the report of the Court of Inquiry shows the position of the fallen girders and train and allows the reader to locate the reference points given by the divers for the positions on the wrecked bridge where they were conducting operations. *House of Lords Record Office; photo Geremy Butler*

Below The composition of the 4.15pm train from Edinburgh to Dundee on 28 December 1879, recording the damage to each part of the train – another diagram from the report of the Court of Inquiry. *House of Lords Record Office; photo Geremy Butler*

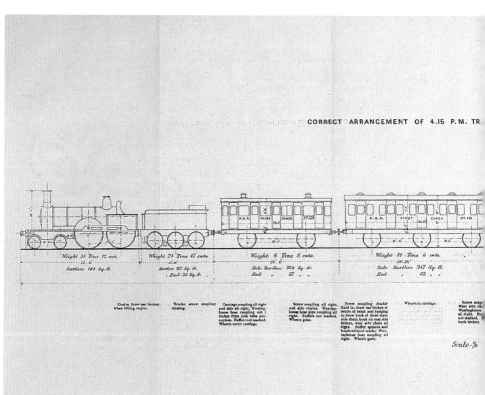

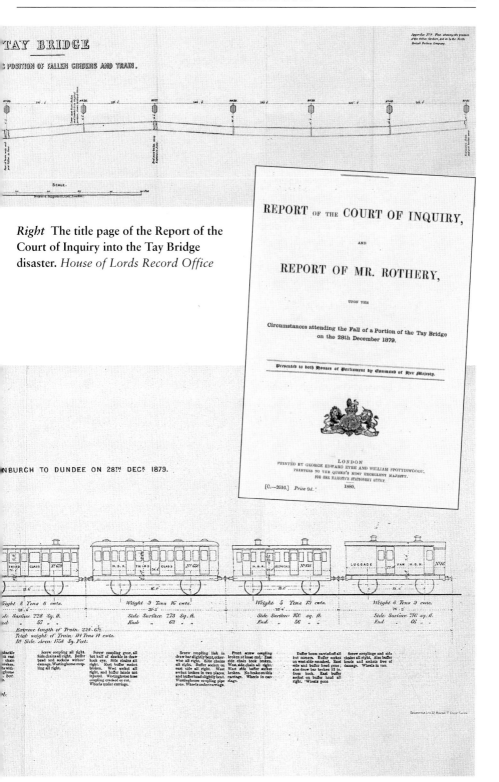

Right The title page of the Report of the
Court of Inquiry into the Tay Bridge
disaster. *House of Lords Record Office*

Distinguished witnesses who gave evidence to the Court of Inquiry: clockwise from top left, Allan Stewart, James Brunlees, Benjamin Baker and Sir Thomas Bouch (1822-1880), designer of the Tay Bridge. *Institution of Civil Engineers*

The last standing pier at the north end of the gap, showing the broken girder and rails, with a hazy view of Dundee beyond. *University of St Andrews*

Above The broken bridge seen from Wormit. *Dundee Central Library*

Below A fallen girder lies in the water. *University of St Andrews*

Above A beached section of the fallen bridge showing the mangled rails and the remains of the railway carriages; this is part of the fifth girder from the south, lying on what was its east side. *Dundee Central Library*

Below A carriage in a wrecked girder. *University of St Andrews*

Above The only survivor of the doomed train: NBR 4-4-0 locomotive No 224, 'The Diver', back on dry land. *Dundee Central Library*

Below A postcard view of the training ship *Mars* in 1905, with the replacement Tay Bridge and the stumps of the old one in the background. *University of St Andrews*

Above A steam launch and divers' barge employed in the search of the wreckage of the Tay Bridge, in an engraving from the *Illustrated London News*, 3 January 1880. *Science Museum*

Below The drama of the diving operations at the fallen bridge is captured in another *Illustrated London News* engraving produced very soon after the bridge had gone down. *Science Museum*

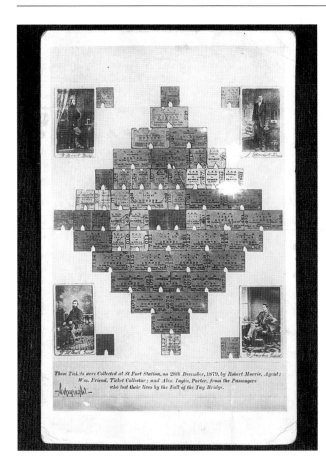

Charles Meik, Bouch's assistant, examined the bridge after its fall, and provided the Court of Inquiry's most detailed account of the condition in which the bridge had been left after it had gone down. The bases on which the cast-iron piers had been erected were in every case brick, and were undamaged. The bridge was not level from end to end, being higher at the south end, and the inclination was not uniform for each pier-span: for example, from pier 38 at the north end there was a rise of 1 in 73.56 to pier 37, then a gentler rise of 1 in 130 to pier 30 and a level run to pier 29. Between pier 29 and pier 6 there was a falling gradient of 1 in 353, followed by another level run to pier 3, and a final rise of 1 in 100 to the south abutment.

Meik's survey after the fall showed that several of the struts and ties of the eastern girder of No 4 span had been bent and broken by something that had impinged upon them, the blows coming towards the north from the south. Meik found peculiar scores in several places on those portions of the girder. He thought there appeared to have been some body scraping over the struts and ties. Generally, the height of some of these horizontal lines upon the girder corresponded to the height of the roof of the carriages, although some were lower.

Interesting marks were also found on two of the carriages, one on the roof of the 2nd Class carriage and the other on the roof of the guard's van. At the first place at which abrasions occurred, the southernmost of those marks, Meik observed that a rivet had been struck out from the girder and the cover had been lifted from a tie by something forcibly parting it. Meik found splinters of wood between the cover and the lattice, and these splinters appeared to have been driven in with very considerable force indeed.

The wrecked train

'Drummond found nothing in the condition of the couplings or buffers to indicate that the train had gone off the line before the bridge went down.'

Dugald Drummond was the Locomotive Superintendent with the North British Railway Company, and as such was well-qualified to comment on the condition of the train as found after the bridge had gone down.

The train comprised the engine and its tender, then one 3rd, one 1st, two 3rd and one 2nd Class carriages, and one brake-van. The engine weighed 34 tons 12 cwt, and the tender 24 tons. The 1st Class carriage weighed 13 tons, and one of the 3rd Class carriages weighed the same, while the two other 3rds weighed 12 tons each. The 2nd Class carriage weighed 10 tons, and the brake-van 12 tons. Thus the total weight of the train was 130 tons 12 cwt.

The whole train, from engine to brake-van, was 254 feet long. The 1st Class carriage alone was 32 feet long, the 2nd Class one 26 feet, and the 3rd Class 28 feet each. The height of the 1st Class carriage was 7 feet inside, and it was 7 feet wide; the framing added about 11 inches to the height, while to the top of the lantern on the carriages the height was some 8 feet in total.

On 15 April 1880 Drummond reported to the solicitors of the North British Railway Company upon the state of the train and the carriages, which he had himself examined at Dundee, especially with regard to position of the regulator and the reversing lever on the engine. He had examined the wrecked train at the first opportunity, and had concluded from that examination that the fall of the bridge could not be attributed to the carriages having smashed against it when they left the rails.

Drummond found the 2nd Class carriage all gone to pieces except the underframe. At the north end of the train every coupling was broken through the centres of the shackles. He did not know what condition the couplings had been in when found, and he feared that the process of bringing them ashore might have damaged them. Drummond also found that the west-side buffer socket was broken, although the buffer on the east side was intact. The buffer head was made of timber, and it was the timber that had broken.

Drummond had never known a carriage upset by the wind, nor had he ever heard of such an event. The theory of the carriages going off the line and breaking through the girders was familiar to Drummond. When he had seen the wrecked 2nd Class carriage his first view was that, if its fore-part had come against the lattice of the bridge and if the carriage had been strong enough to resist the impact, it would have turned at an angle and would have presented its easternmost side to the brake-van behind it. In point of fact, the greatest amount of damage was to the west side; the east side of the framework was entire when Drummond inspected it, while the west side was all smashed.

Drummond thought that if the 1st Class carriage had come in contact with the latticework the carriage would not have been strong enough to have resisted the impact so as to have sent it round; it would have gone off at once, like matchwood, and would have left no indications at all on the girders. If the 2nd Class carriage had been tilted by the lateral force of the wind so as to bring its easternmost corner in contact with the latticework, it would have fallen below its natural level on the rails. Drummond thought that the bending of the axles he had discovered could only be accounted for by the girder going over the longitudinals to which the rails were fixed; the axles he examined had been bent in towards the centre.

Drummond found nothing in the condition of the couplings or buffers to indicate that the train had gone off the line before the bridge went down. He did not think that any of the carriages left the rails until the girders had left their places on the pillars, a view he had formed after carefully looking over the state of the equipment.

Drummond had not taken any trouble to make any calculation with a view to ascertaining what would have been the effect of the sudden arresting of the momentum of two carriages by the latticework of the girder. He was quite sure that the tie-bars would have destroyed the carriage, a view formed simply from his knowledge of the construction of the carriages.

Drummond had found that the steam of the engine had not been shut off, and the brakes had not been applied. There was every indication that there had been no time for action by the train's crew. The reversing lever was standing at the third notch from the centre, or six notches from full forward gear; the regulator was standing full open; the brake screw on the tender was full off; and the brake screw on the brake-van at the rear of the train was also off. Those facts were indications of great suddenness in the character of the accident. The first thing a driver would do if there was anything wrong, if he felt any jolting with his engine, would be to shut the regulator; this action was second nature, as drivers had to do it so often when the engine was slipping in wet weather. It was the first thing they would do before attempting to put on the brake. The engine had a Westinghouse automatic air brake, which was operated by the driver; it was not fitted to the guard's van.

10
WHY THE BRIDGE WENT DOWN

The Engineers

'The bridge showed itself to be remarkably stiff and rigid:
it bore its tests remarkably well.'

The Court of Inquiry sought and obtained expert advice on the possible causes of the bridge's fall, and this came from a number of engineers. The Court appointed one, Henry Law, to carry out a specialist survey of the bridge's design and the role of wind pressure in its fall. Naturally the Court took evidence from Sir Thomas Bouch, the bridge's engineer, but it also heard from other engineers, who had great experience in bridge design.

A common underlying theme of the engineers' evidence was whether, and how much, allowance had been made for the effects of wind pressure, and therefore what strength of wind pressure any bridge should be designed to withstand. The Court of Inquiry heard that there was a great variation in practice in the extent of allowance for wind pressure among different engineers worldwide.

The most important engineer from whom the Court of Inquiry heard evidence was Sir Thomas Bouch himself. In the course of the bridge's construction he had often examined it, and was convinced from his most careful examination that the work was all in perfectly good order. If he had found any inferior work, he would have rejected it.

Bouch had given a great deal of very anxious thought as to why his bridge had gone down, and his consideration led him to conclude that the reason for the bridge's fall was the capsizing of the last or the second-last carriage and the van. He thought that they had canted over against the leeward girder (that facing away from the wind) and come into collision with it. Bouch had no doubt that, in his judgement, such a collision, at the speed at which the train was going, would have been sufficient to destroy the bridge. In practice, the first blow would have been the momentum of the whole train, until the couplings broke. In Bouch's view, taking the body of the train going at that speed it would have destroyed anything.

Bouch thought it significant that the 2nd Class carriage and the van were on their sides when found under water, as was the engine. He accounted for the remaining four carriages being on their wheels by the fact that, as they went into the water together, the principal weight was on the wheels and the axles, so flotation would therefore turn them up.

The 2nd Class carriage was completely destroyed. All the top of the carriage was gone, so there was nothing to float, and it might have been entangled with the girder. In the case of the van, the same thing applied: the east side next to the girder had entirely gone. The framework of the carriage was all smashed, and the van's side was entirely gone. The footboards on the east side of the carriage were gone, as if they had struck against something. In the case of most of the girders that were lifted after the accident, the permanent way was visible, and the girders were not much damaged, excepting here and there.

There was another thing that Bouch thought conclusive, which was that the 2nd Class carriage had lost an axle-box by being forced against the side of a girder. The iron guide in which the axle-box moved was broken off on the east side, and the axle-box was found in the trough of the girder. It could not have got there unless the girder had been standing – it must have gone into the trough before the girder fell. Another fact was that the wind necessary to overturn the 2nd Class carriage was a great deal less than would have been necessary to blow down the bridge. If a wind pressure of 40lb per square foot were to blow down the bridge, it would have upturned the carriages long before.

In the debris between piers Nos 3 and 4, Bouch had observed, the permanent way was all twisted and the chairs that anchored the rail sleepers were all broken. The girders themselves were broken, and there were marks on them, which unmistakably proved that the train had been in contact with them. This meant, Bouch thought, that the scorings had been made by the rubbing of the roofs of the carriages along the lattice of the girder, and that the breaking of one bracing and the bending of some others had also been so caused. The lattice bracing was broken and curled. The carriage and the van, he believed, had therefore struck at that point.

Bouch accordingly believed that when the previous train had crossed the bridge there had been great friction between the carriage wheels and the guard-rail, and that had caused the production of sparks observed by people on that train. The direction of the wind, Bouch thought, was slightly behind the carriages as well as to the side – south-west by west – and therefore violently forced the carriage to leeward at that time.

Bouch thought that the fact that on previous trains a certain tilting of the carriages had been observed indicated that the force of the wind was approaching the overturning point. However, the force of the wind did not affect the last train before the bridge fell to the same extent. There was no doubt that when the doomed train passed onto the bridge the wind was very much stronger than when the previous train had crossed.

Bouch thought it significant that the 2nd Class carriage was an exceptionally light one and was very much smashed: the body had gone entirely and the framework behind was so thoroughly broken that Bouch thought it had been broken when it had been struck by the van coming behind it.

Importantly, the Court of Inquiry observed that the great majority of railway structures, brick, masonry and iron, were built with no special provision for wind pressure, because the weight and lateral strength imparted to such structures was sufficient, due to dead weight and load, to be more than adequate to meet any lateral wind pressure. Bouch had therefore provided amply for dead weight and moving loads in the Tay Bridge. He did not consider it necessary to make special provision for wind pressure.

Allan Stewart (1831-94) was, like Bouch, a civil engineer. He had graduated from Cambridge University in 1853 and worked initially for the firm of Messrs Blyth of Edinburgh, engineers of the Caledonian Railway. They had the largest engineering business in Scotland, and while there he had worked a great deal for Benjamin Hall Blyth, the eminent railway engineer, before becoming independent.

Stewart had done a great deal of work for Bouch, particularly in checking the calculations of many of his most important works. He it was who worked out the details and calculations for Bouch's Edinburgh Bridge, which was a rather complicated bridge, a combination of a suspension bridge with a continuous girder. Stewart also went on to do a great part of the work for the design of the Forth Bridge, including the calculation of all the strains.

Stewart assisted the engineer William Barlow in the calculations necessary for the latter's report to the Tay Bridge inquiry. Barlow was one of the leading structural engineers of the time, and sat on the Court of Inquiry. He also went on to be engineer of the replacement Tay Bridge.

In 1869 Stewart was assisting Bouch in the designs and calculations for the girders for the Tay Bridge. He prepared all the designs for the girders, under Bouch's instructions, consulting him with regard to many matters of detail before the Bill that gave authority to build the Tay Bridge went to Parliament. Stewart was also frequently consulted by Bouch on questions that arose during the progress of the work. At Bouch's request he frequently attended meetings between Bouch and the contractors and others, and they discussed all questions about the foundations and other parts of the piers.

Stewart was consulted with regard to the design for the superstructure, for which there had not been many plans. The spans had been altered and Stewart had prepared detailed drawings under Bouch's instruction. The relative advantages of an eight-column and a six-column structure were discussed on more than one occasion. Stewart favoured the six-column design, which was ultimately adopted.

In 1875 Stewart attended a very large number of meetings, both at Bouch's office and at the bridge, but chiefly at the bridge, and was accompanied Bouch upwards of 20 times during that year in visits to the bridge. He kept a diary that recorded that the thickness of the columns was decided upon on 6 April 1875. That day Bouch decided to make the iron of the outer columns 1¼ inches, and that of the inner columns 1 inch thick. He instructed the contractors accordingly.

Stewart attended Major General Hutchinson's final examination to approve the bridge for the Board of Trade. He had seen the bridge at various times during the progress of the work, and although he did not inspect the workmanship in great detail, so far as the general features and appearances went he thought the bridge certainly satisfactorily put together.

Stewart thought Hutchinson's tests were of a very careful and exceptionally strict character. Nearly every girder and pier was tested, and the bridge showed itself to be remarkably stiff and rigid: it bore its tests remarkably well. The deflections of the girders were far less than he had anticipated, and the piers were very rigid and free from oscillation or vibration. It was a very well designed structure and very well put together. Stewart visited the bridge after its fall and saw nothing that led him to believe that it had failed through the inferiority of the workmanship or construction.

Stewart thought that it would have required something more than any particular wind pressure that one could have expected upon the bridge to have caused what happened on the night of 28 December. He certainly thought that the shock of two carriages going at a speed of 25mph, if they came into collision with a girder, on top of all the normal strains upon the bridge, would have been sufficient to have caused the failure of the bridge that night.

Stewart had considered the question of the uprooting of the columns, which he thought was a different question from lateral sheering (the tendency of one column to slide over the other). Stewart thought it would be absolutely impossible that the sheering or lateral shifting of the columns under the circumstances, and with the pressure that the wind could bring upon them, could have caused the fracture of the bridge.

Stewart had calculated that a wind pressure of 75lb per square foot would have been sufficient to destroy the bridge by the uprooting of the windward columns. His calculations showed that the resistance of the bolts at the flanges of each column to uprooting was far in excess of the forces that he had assumed on account of the flexure of the columns. The columns were perfectly firm to resist flexure to the extent that Stewart had credited them with in his calculation.

Stewart calculated that the weight was up to 2.3 tons upon each of the 18-inch columns, and 1.06 tons upon each of the 15-inch columns – about 20 foot-tons at the bottom of each column. This was no more than a fifth of the overturning force that would uproot the bolts, and at that point the ties would have gone. It had been suggested that there was a certain amount of loosening of some of the tie-bars, and that a chattering was observed after the bridge had been opened for some time, and that those loose tie-bars had been cottered up, or made firm, in a certain number of instances with the aid of packing pieces, and that had left the bridge all tight.

Benjamin Baker (1840-1907) was another leading Victorian railway engineer called upon to comment on Bouch's engineering of the Tay Bridge. Baker's most prominent engineering achievement was to be the first railway bridge over the Firth of Forth, completed in 1890. This was a cantilever bridge that for several years was to be the world's longest span, almost 1½ miles in length. His calculations of wind pressure in the Firth of Forth took account of the Tay Bridge disaster, principally in making due allowance for wind pressure, which Bouch and the inspector of railways in 1878-79 had not. William Morris, the designer and craftsman whose designs revolutionised Victorian taste, declared the Forth Bridge 'the supremest specimen of all ugliness', in contrast to Bouch's 'beautiful railway bridge of the silv'ry Tay' (William McGonagall)! Baker appeared 128 times before Parliamentary Committees on Bills to promote railways he engineered.

In contrast to Bouch, Baker thought that the carriages would not have damaged the girders at all, but he could imagine that in a very high state of tension the lugs, with a comparatively slight jar, could have failed.

John Cochrane (1823-91) was a noted civil engineer of the Victorian era. He superintended the construction of a number of bridges and viaducts, and in that capacity gave evidence to the Court of Inquiry. The most notable works he was involved in included the Crystal Palace for the Great Exhibition of 1851 and the Clifton suspension bridge in Bristol. In 1855 he built the bridge over the Thames at Westminster, and was involved in Charing Cross and Cannon Street bridges in London. He was therefore well-qualified to comment on Bouch's work on the Tay Bridge.

In his view the disaster arose from the extraordinary pressure of the wind on the night of the storm, and he thought that in the action of that wind and previous winds, a great many of the bolts connecting the diagonal ties of the columns may have been bent – indeed, probably were bent. That would cause considerable lateral movement in the pier, and Cochrane was convinced that, if the pier had been kept rigidly upright, it would have been strong enough for its purpose.

In Cochrane's view that vital rigidity became much diminished the moment one began to increase the distance between the centres of the bolts in the lug at the top of a column and the lug at the bottom of its adjacent column. That the bolts had been bent was indicated by the shaking of the tie-bars. Upwards of 100 packings had been put in during the construction of the bridge, where the contractors had found a shaking. If they had found no shaking at all and nothing loose, then Cochrane would have concluded that the bolts had not bent; but on the night of the great storm Cochrane thought that the probability was that the pressure of the wind had bent them all, right up to the top.

Cochrane thought that there was some probability that some of these bolts had bent before the night of the great storm. Indeed, he thought that was highly probable, because there had been heavy gales there since the structure had been erected, beside the exceptionally heavy gale on the night the bridge went down.

In Cochrane's opinion, the yielding of the bolts contributed materially to the disaster, and he thought it exceedingly doubtful that it could have been discovered even by a careful examination of the bridge. Additionally, he observed that the chattering of the bars certainly indicated looseness. Unfortunately, he was very sorry that, when these bars were found to be loose from the yielding of the bolts, the mode of packing adopted was, in his opinion, not the best mode of remedying what had taken place. As a man of skill, Cochrane was quite clear what course he would have adopted if he had discovered the ties giving by the bending of the bolts. He would have immediately communicated with the chief engineer, and called his attention to the point, with a view to devising some means of preventing the possibility of its recurring.

Cochrane had not heard any observation made as to the effect of the upward force of the wind on the girders, but he thought it was an element that should decidedly have been taken into consideration. The upward force of wind was a thing that any engineer had to guard against more than anything else in large suspension bridges. Overall, Cochrane considered that the bridge had not fallen as a result of the action of the train upon it. His view was that the three eastern columns had given way first, followed by the three western columns. He thought that it was a question of the bracing: if the columns had been strongly braced by angle-girders the bridge would not have fallen.

The contractors' engineer was Albert Gröthe. He believed that the shock of two of the carriages going along at the rate of 25mph, if they came into collision with the girders, superimposed on all the normal restraints upon the bridge, would certainly have been sufficient to cause a failure of the bridge.

Henry Law was a prolific railway engineer. He gave evidence in Parliament on 69 Bills for railways he engineered, including the London, Brighton & South Coast Railway and the South Eastern Railway. He was a member of the Institution of Civil Engineers, and was called upon by the Court of Inquiry to investigate the plans for the fallen bridge. He spent three days at the bridge, inspecting it with John Cochrane and one of Sir Thomas Bouch's assistants.

Law believed that Bouch's design, if properly carried out, was sufficient to meet the strains that would come upon it, without an excess of wind. He could not say that it was designed to meet the strongest wind; however, he could say that it was designed to meet 40lb per square foot pressure, which is what he calculated would be needed to overturn one of the piers.

Law believed that it would not have been necessary for the wind to extend over the whole of that part of the bridge that had fallen. It would probably have been sufficient that the wind was upon part of it, upon some part of the high girders. He accordingly considered that the cause of the accident was the excessive force of the lateral strain placed upon the structure, and also thought it probable that the first element to contribute to the accident was the bending of some of the bolts.

Nevertheless, Law reaffirmed that the structure was amply strong for its purpose. The principal qualification to his answer was that he was not in a position – not having calculated it – to say whether the tension-bars were of sufficient area and strength to take the tensions that would come upon them in extreme cases. He simply could not say whether they were or not.

Law acknowledged that in all probability there never was a bridge, or indeed a structure of any kind carried into effect by any engineer, that other engineers would not have made in a different way, and thought they improved it by so doing.

James Brunlees (1816-92) was another prominent civil engineer, who had given evidence in Parliament on railway Bills 150 times in his lifetime. He engineered various railways in extreme natural conditions, and did a great deal of work in Brazil. He engineered a viaduct a mile long over the shifting sands of the Solway Firth, and with John Hawkshaw he engineered the first Channel Tunnel scheme (1872-86). He was asked to visit the scene of the fall of the bridge with Cochrane for the purpose of examining both the quality of the material used and the workmanship, and also to give an opinion as to the probable cause of the disaster. Brunlees had had considerable experience of building bridges, with cast-iron piers and wrought-iron superstructures over a 27-year period. His bridges totalled more than 4 miles in length.

On both his visits to Dundee Brunlees went over the ruins of the bridge in company with John Cochrane and one of Bouch's assistants. He agreed with Cochrane's evidence that the design, if properly carried out, was sufficient to meet the strains that would come upon it; it was sufficient so long as there was not an excess of wind. Brunlees could not say that it was designed to meet the strongest wind; he would say, however, that it was designed to meet 40lb of pressure, which, like Law, is what he believed it would take to overturn one of the piers with a train upon it.

Brunlees found it impossible to say what the highest pressure of wind was that he would have expected to have to provide against over a large surface. He believed the upheaving effect of the wind upon the platform had not been taken account of. He also thought that extremes of wind pressure ought to have been taken into account in the calculations, but had not.

He pondered whether, in the course of his experience, he had had any experience that might have led him to believe that such a pressure as 40lb of wind over a structure of the size of the Tay Bridge had ever been observed or was to be expected. Like Law, he observed that it would not be necessary for the wind to extend over the whole part of the bridge that had fallen. He also observed that a good deal less than 40lb of wind would blow a tree down, depending very much upon the tree and the soil in which it was rooted.

Brunlees emphasised how unique the storm had been on the night of 28 December 1879. He had never experienced or observed any storm that would lead him to believe that anything approaching 40lb of wind had been experienced over a surface as large as one of the spans of the Tay Bridge. In his experience, for the roofs of buildings engineers had taken 30lb of wind pressure as the maximum that had to be withstood.

Brunlees considered cases when he had constructed bridges with larger spans. He had constructed one viaduct in Brazil 170 feet high, and there he had no occasion to reckon anything for the wind, because the viaduct was placed across a small ravine running into the main valley, and in that case he had the wind coming end-on to the viaduct. In point of fact, Brunlees acknowledged that he had never had occasion, in his experience, to consider what would be the allowance for wind that one would have to provide for in the case of a structure like the Tay Bridge.

Henry Law's report for the Commissioners on the effect of wind upon the Tay Bridge had shown that it would have taken a much higher pressure of wind to have overturned the bridge. The result Law came to was that it would take 64.38lb per square foot of wind to overturn the structure, treating the pier as rigid and the columns as bolted down.

In Brunlees's opinion, the holding-down bolts were never called into play, although they were no doubt disturbed in the falling of the structure. Regarding the pier as a rigid structure, it was obvious that the fact of it being anchored by bolts or anything else on the windward side was not to be neglected in considering what would overturn it. However, the bridge was overturned at a higher level, and the bolts were simply disturbed by the falling of the columns and the girders. Brunlees assumed that the tie-bars were efficient, and that the pier turned over as one complete, rigid structure.

Henry Law believed that the tension upon those bolts was so great that it split some of the stones. Brunlees did not agree: he considered that the stones had split in the falling of the structure.

John Cochrane had raised the question as to whether the last two carriages of the train had come into collision with the girder. Brunlees observed that he had seen the whole of what remained of the wrecked train, but he had not seen anything that would lead him to infer that any of the carriages had been derailed – he had examined them most carefully. However, the two last carriages were smashed up in a way that the others were not. The 2nd Class carriage especially was very severely smashed, but then Brunlees observed that those carriages were very much smashed in the lifting, even though the evidence of the divers had suggested that they were in that smashed condition before they were lifted. Brunlees thought that might have happened without the 2nd Class carriage having run into the girder; he believed that the carriage must have been stopped by something, not necessarily by the girder. He did not think it was stopped by the fore-part of the train.

Brunlees's views suggested to the Commissioners that the carriage must have been stopped by part of the bridge, as there was nothing else there to stop it. However, in the last carriages Brunlees found that the foot-boards were knocked off, and the irons that supported the foot-boards had been all bent towards the tail end of the train on the eastern side. Then, going round to the west side, Brunlees had found exactly the same thing, namely, that the irons were bent back towards the tail of the train.

Brunlees did not think the carriage and its framing would have been strong enough to have tilted the train off. Nor did he think that any blow upon the body of a carriage poised upon two sets of wheels would turn them off the rails. He could not think of any consideration that suggested to him there might have been such a collision. Account had to be taken of the fact that the guard's van was very much heavier than the 2nd Class carriage, and would be very likely to run into it and knock it about a good deal.

Brunlees further believed there could not have been a collision between the guard's van and the 2nd Class carriage in front of it unless the velocity of the 2nd Class carriage had been arrested before that of the guard's van. The 2nd Class carriage must of necessity have been arrested by some means or other – but by what means one could not tell. The 2nd Class carriage, or its frames, were broken on both sides, showing that something had gone into the frames and pitched very violently against them.

Brunlees closely examined the materials of which the bridge had been composed. On the first occasion when he had visited the fallen piers, he had taken a sample of the iron of every pier from the remains that he found, and in almost every case he found the iron to be of very good quality. He had had great experience in the use of cast-iron in columns and structures such as the Tay Bridge and had the most thorough confidence in its use, based not only on theoretical opinion, but upon large and long practical experience. Brunlees believed that cast-iron columns formed a satisfactory pier for a structure of this kind. His view on the relative safety of cast-iron columns to brick piers was that, all other things being equal, he should just as soon use cast-iron as brick.

Brunlees had an opinion on the carriages immediately before the 2nd Class carriage, which had been found after the accident on their wheels, standing upright. The girder had been thrown upon its side, which showed that the carriages must have turned up and righted themselves, as the air and water would float them up while the wheels and axles acted as ballast. No doubt they would rise up against the girder; Brunlees thought that the tops of the carriages had struck the top of the girder which now lay on its side.

If the train had become derailed before the bridge was disturbed, the top of the carriage could hardly have struck the top of the girder, considering that the girder was about 27 feet high. It must have happened after the girder fell. Similarly with the engine and tender – the girder was very much broken.

Turning to wind pressure, if Brunlees had assumed that a wind pressure of 30lb had to be allowed for when constructing a bridge, he would not have built a bridge with that strength exactly so it would be upset by just 31lb. Brunlees would probably have given a margin of five times that, for a pressure of 120lb. He would certainly not have built his bridge so that it would have been upset by an extra pound of pressure.

As for the iron, it would have been four or five times stronger than would have been needed to resist successfully the anticipated wind pressure that would come upon it. Brunlees thought that a wind pressure of 40lb would have upset the pier, but not the whole structure, even allowing for the strength of the iron.

Brunlees held to his first view, that the train did not leave the rails until the bridge began to give way. He saw nothing to suggest that it had done. The carriage might have come into collision with the bridge's latticework after the bridge had given way. When one came to the question of overturning a pier, it was not a question of strain upon the ironwork, but it no doubt was a question of the width of the base. Were Brunlees to be called upon to reconstruct the Tay Bridge, he would have made the base of these piers four times bigger than they were.

When Brunlees had built his tall viaduct in Brazil, 170 feet in height, the top was 15 feet wide within the rails, and he had two raking columns on each side, having an inclination of 1 in 12 on each side, making the total width of the base 45 feet. The height of the Tay Bridge being 85 feet to the rails, he would have put the same inclination upon the raker (an inclined beam or strut) as he had done in the other case. The viaduct in Brazil was constructed with iron castings and wrought-iron ties, and was to that extent similar to the Tay Bridge.

Brunlees could not recall much written work on bridge engineering that treated the question of wind pressure. Some work had been done by the Institution of Civil Engineers on the subject of wind pressure affecting the Menai Bridge in Wales, which had been constructed to resist a wind pressure of some 50lb. The platform was very much given to rise during heavy gales, and the roadway was strengthened to correct that. There were no rules that could be applied to the question of wind pressure – there was no rule that said what pressure one should take on the second girder, assuming a certain pressure on the first. Brunlees did not know what the rules were in the United States or in France.

The Inspectors of Railways

'The design was not unsatisfactory. There was nothing in the design in his judgment to warrant his objecting in any way to it.'

Under the legislative controls on railway development, all new schemes had to be inspected by a Board of Trade inspector. The fate of the Tay Bridge showed that these arrangements were not adequate. All that the law required was that the Officers of the Board of Trade should say, not whether the design was good and the work constructed on the best principles, nor whether there were or were not any latent defects in it, but whether they could give any good reason why a bridge should not be opened for passenger traffic.

Major General Charles Scrope Hutchinson had received instructions from the Board of Trade to inspect the Tay Bridge in February 1878, and accordingly visited the bridge on the 25th, 26th and 27th of that month. Sir Thomas Bouch was with him during his inspection, and Hutchinson's report was submitted to the Board of Trade from Newcastle, dated 5 March 1878, barely a week after the inspection.

After setting out the terms of his appointment, Hutchinson described the powers granted to the Tay Bridge Railway, in conjunction with the Forth Bridge Railway, for which an Act of Parliament had been obtained. The Tay Bridge would shorten the existing route between Edinburgh and Dundee, via Stirling, by 28 miles, and by means of these two railways and a new railway about to be constructed between Arbroath and Montrose, the journey between Edinburgh and Aberdeen would be reduced by 23 miles.

In consequence of the magnitude of this bridge it had been considered desirable to have it inspected before the lines north and south of it were ready for traffic. The inspection of the bridge accordingly took place over three days, the weather, fortunately, being favourable.

At about the same time that Hutchinson had been receiving his instructions from the Board of Trade, he had received drawings and descriptions accompanying the application of the company for the inspection. It was absolutely normal practice to get such drawings prior to any inspection. Hutchinson then went to Dundee, where he saw Edgar Gilkes, one of the contractors; all the information that he required was given by the contractors.

He then began by making a general examination of the whole of the bridge, both above and below. The dimensions of the various parts of the girders had been carefully worked out, and in no case had the iron been submitted to a greater strain than 5 tons to the inch. Upon careful examination of the brickwork and masonry, they appeared to be of a substantial character, and to be showing no signs of settlement. The ironwork had been well put together, both in the columns and the girders.

Then, having made that general inspection, his next work was to test the bridge for deflection and oscillation. For this purpose the North British Railway Company placed at his disposal six new goods engines, each weighing 73 tons and measuring 48½ feet, the total weight employed being thus 438 tons, and the total length of the engines being 291 feet, which rather more than covered one of the 245-foot spans, and represented as nearly as possible 1½ tons to the running foot.

Each girder was tested, step by step, beginning at the south end, by placing upon the bridge one engine, two engines, three engines, four engines, five engines and finally six engines at a time, and running them at various speeds. Hutchinson thought the maximum speed they ran at was probably 45mph. He then observed, as well as he could, what lateral oscillation the high girders might have, by stationing himself some distance off and directing a theodolite (a surveying instrument for measuring horizontal and vertical angles) on the top of the girders. Hutchinson also did this on the top of one of the columns, and observed what amount of lateral oscillation there was with the engine running over at speed. The result was very satisfactory: the lateral oscillation seemed almost nil, there being a very slight divergence from the perpendicular.

On the third day of his inspection Hutchinson went underneath the bridge in a small steam launch with a small boat; he landed on a good many piers and climbed about the columns. He was even slung up inside one of the piers under the high girders and taken to the very top in order to examine the condition of the ties from top to bottom. At the same time the engines were again running over the bridge to enable him to see what amount of vibration there was, and what kind of behaviour the columns presented. He observed nothing at all to give him an uncomfortable impression about the stability of the columns.

There was naturally a slight vibration in the tie-bars as the engines ran over, but nothing more than one would always find in every structure; there was nothing at all excessive as far as Hutchinson's judgement went. He examined at the same time, as far as he was able to do so, the attachment of all the different parts; he could not have looked at each bolt in each pier, as that would have taken far more time than he had at his disposal.

To that point, Hutchinson's examination was enough in his judgement, then and subsequently, to satisfy his own mind and to enable him to make the report that he made to the Board of Trade, that the bridge could be opened for the passage of trains. He observed no symptoms of weakness that to his judgement gave any reason to doubt the stability of the structure; this always pre-supposed, Hutchinson said, that the materials of which it was constructed were good, and that the workmanship was good, and that it was properly maintained. Hutchinson added that in his opinion the materials and the workmanship were good. However, this view would not be shared by the Court of Inquiry.

Hutchinson had no doubt that the action of the trains crossing the bridge would naturally tend to loosen cotters to some extent. The higher the speeds, the greater the racking motion produced on the structure. This was a factor that had contributed to his recommending a speed limit on the bridge of 25mph. The bridge was not a structure with a wide base, and therefore it was very desirable to limit the action of passing trains.

The tendency of the cotters to loosen would have been enhanced by high winds blowing across the bridge. If Hutchinson had found any cotters in a condition that would have necessitated the insertion of a packing piece, he would have called attention to it and would have requested that the bar in question be tightened or replaced by a proper one, but the presence of two or three loose bars – had he seen them – would not have led him to think that the bridge was an imperfect bridge, and should not be passed.

In his report Hutchinson had observed, 'When again visiting the spot I should wish, if possible, to have the opportunity of observing the effects of high wind when a train of carriages was running over the bridge.' During the time that Hutchinson was at Dundee at the end of February, it so happened that there was no high wind blowing and he was, therefore, anxious to see what additional or perceptible effect a high wind on a train of carriages might have had.

Before an opportunity arose for that further inspection, Hutchinson was taken seriously ill, and the final inspection of the railways north and south of the bridge devolved upon another officer. In February he had been expecting to be able to go back to the bridge for further inspection of the new lines, and meant to have spent some little time in Dundee with the hope of getting the opportunity of observing the effect of a gale upon the bridge. That such a full inspection never took place might be considered to have contributed directly to the bridge opening when it was not capable of successfully resisting the wind on the night it went down.

With regard to the details of construction, Hutchinson had taken every precaution that he could at the time he was underneath the bridge when the trains were passing over by clasping the columns and by various experiments to ascertain what amount of vibration or jar there was. This he did in a good many of them, though not in all; he climbed and held onto the columns and the braces when the engines were going over.

Hutchinson was asked by the Court of Inquiry if, in considering structures of this kind, he had adopted any rule or practice as to what wind pressure ought to be provided for. He had not – he had no data whatever to go upon with regard to wind pressure. He had never heard of any number being adopted, except in the case of the Forth Bridge, and there he had understood that upon the authority of the Astronomer Royal it was considered that 10lb per square foot distributed over a large surface was the amount that might reasonably be expected in Great Britain.

It had never been, to the best of Hutchinson's knowledge, customary hitherto to take wind pressure into account in calculating stresses on bridges of this description. According to his previous knowledge, and with all he knew on the subject, apart from anything that might have been learned from this actual disaster, Hutchinson could not suggest a figure for wind pressure to be allowed for – he had no knowledge to go upon.

While Hutchinson himself did not recollect the exact speed at which the engines were run over the bridge, he had no doubt that it was about 40mph. He well remembered that some engines were coupled and the contractor, Mr Gilkes, suggesting to him that they should come over at a speed of 40mph.

When Hutchinson inspected the bridge it had been completed and painted, so he could only see it superficially; he could not test whether or not the bolts were sufficient, nor if the bolt holes were of proper construction. One could only judge by outside appearances if one had any reason to suppose that anything was wrong, which might have led him to take out a tie-bar and examine it. So when he had said he examined the attachment of the parts in their different places, he meant so far as he could see it externally.

Hutchinson's opinion was that, having regard to the fact that the piers had a narrow base for their height and therefore would be liable to a racking motion, he had thought it prudent that the speeds of trains should be limited. The speed limit he proposed was to apply to any part of a train's journey on any part of the bridge, his object being to restrain the speed to a low limit in the centre of the bridge, where otherwise it would tend to be high.

Hutchinson was quite satisfied during his examination of the bridge on 25, 26 and 27 February that he found it a stiff structure, and at that time the Tay Bridge was fit to open, with the exception of some details. He intended only to examine it again in the sense of trying to see the effect upon the stiffness of the piers of a high wind with a train on the bridge.

Hutchinson had set out only the following requirements: first, that transoms and ties for preserving the gauge should be provided between the longitudinals; second, the fireproof covering of the floor required repair in several places; and third, some slack places in the rails required adjusting. To reduce as much as possible the expansion of the girders in hot weather, Hutchinson strongly recommended their being painted white. Also, he thought it would not be desirable that trains should run over the bridge at a high speed, and he suggested 25 miles per hour as a limit that should not be exceeded. A certificate would, of course, have to be given that the single line should be worked with the train staff and block telegraph system. Hutchinson warned that very careful attention would be required to ascertain from time to time that no scouring action was taking place in the foundations, particularly in the case of those piers that were subjected to a strong current.

Subject to the above requirements and remarks, Hutchinson concluded that he saw no reason why as soon as the adjoining railways had been completed and inspected, the Board of Trade should object to the railway on the Tay Bridge being used for passengers. The engineer Allan Stewart thought Hutchinson's tests were of a very careful and exceptionally strict character.

The Commissioners suggested to Hutchinson that, looking to the bridge's construction, apart from the wind, it would have been his duty to have examined it subsequently after a lapse of six or eight months. Hutchinson said that was not in his mind at all; he considered that it was quite strong enough for the purpose for which it was intended, apart from wind pressure. However, with regard to the wind pressure he should have liked to have had the opportunity to have examined the bridge again. This desire was not strong enough to have justified him withholding his certificate – he thought the bridge sufficiently strong for the purpose.

Hutchinson acknowledged that he made no calculations at all when the plans were given to him as to what force of wind would be sufficient to overturn the bridge. The subject of wind pressure did not enter into the calculations he made on this occasion, and never had done. He believed that wind pressure had never hitherto entered into civil engineers' calculations. He knew that in France there were some rules, but it had never hitherto been customary in Great Britain, as far as he was aware, to consider this question, especially in an open structure like the Tay Bridge.

Colonel William Yolland (1810-85) was another Board of Trade inspector who inspected the Tay Bridge. He was noted for strictness but not harshness in his investigations. Yolland was an inspector for a long time, from 1854 to 1877, then he became chief inspector until 1885. He was one of the Commissioners appointed to inquire into the causes of the accident on the Tay Bridge.

Yolland told the Commissioners that the attention of the Board of Trade had been called for some time to the question of the construction of long viaducts. In particular, they had examined the construction of long viaducts originally constructed in wood. Some railway companies had been taking steps to construct them in a more durable material, and proposals came before the Board of Trade in some cases that they should be constructed of brick or stone, with parapet walls outside. Yolland was an expert in the use of guard-rails and parapets on bridges, and had examined the causes of a number of accidents before he was given the task of investigating the fall of the Tay Bridge.

Yolland affirmed that the Tay Bridge line was a most important line of communication for east coast traffic in Scotland, and the advantages of the construction of a stable work like the Tay Bridge across the estuary of the Tay were incontrovertible. However, it had been his duty to point out that all single lines were subject to special dangers that had led to some of the most lamentable disasters that there had been. These had resulted from the fallibility of human beings; mistakes had been made in committing two trains to travel on a single line in opposite directions. In the case of a collision between meeting trains on such a site as the Tay Bridge it was impossible to say what would have been the result. It had been upon that ground that Yolland had held that it was a matter of safety in the first instance: if it was worthwhile to construct a viaduct across the Tay, it should have been constructed throughout for a double line of way, although he acknowledged that such a course would have added to the bridge's cost.

Yolland again drew the Commissioners' attention to the importance of any viaduct – whether on land or across a river – having a parapet erected for the purpose of preventing all risk of a train being blown off the rails. He favoured a parapet of about 4ft 6in above the level of the rails for stone or brick viaducts.

Yolland also observed that supposing that proper precautions had been taken regarding wind pressures and the mode of cross-bracing and things of that kind, he would have said that there was no part of the Tay Bridge that was actually so safe for ordinary travelling as between the high girders. Yolland felt bound to say that he hoped that in the future engineers would give up the idea of placing their permanent way on the tops of girders with nothing more than a bit of gas-pipe or a slight hand-rail outside. He felt that it was perfectly impossible to say that mishaps might not occur.

Yolland maintained that engineers generally believed that they could make a better structure by having the permanent way above the girders than at the bottom of those girders, as in the case of the Tay Bridge. Significantly, by that method they could also make a cheaper construction, but he did not share this view on reducing the cost of bridges.

As on other railways, in those days an employee of the railway walked every inch of the track each day looking for faults. George Murray was such an inspector of the permanent way in the service of the North British Railway Company, and had been based at the Tay Bridge since it opened for traffic. He lived in Dundee, and his district extended from Dundee station south from the Tay Bridge to Leuchars, a distance of 6 miles.

It was Murray's duty to keep the permanent way in perfect order, or, if he found it out of order, to have it put into order at once. It was his responsibility to inspect the permanent way of the bridge, and he did this every other day. This he did by walking along and seeing that every baulk and key was tight on the rail, and seeing that the points at each end were in proper working order.

The signals were not entirely under his inspection, but under that of the signalmen. If Murray saw anything wrong with a signal when he was passing, he would report it to the signalman at once. Murray had last inspected the permanent way of the Tay Bridge on Friday 26 December, and had walked along it from south to north at about 11 o'clock in the morning, inspecting it with his usual care.

Murray had found everything correct on his inspection. He saw no frost on the bridge at all that day – a severe frost was apt to affect the line, and the railway would get somewhat slack. However, that night there had been no frost whatever. The weather had been fresh, open weather for some time before. Murray had crossed the bridge more than once when there had been a high wind, which occurred often on the Tay.

Murray had never found the bridge swinging or shaking with the wind. He had never felt any difference, so far as he could judge by walking over it, between the stability of the bridge where it ran over the girders and that part of the bridge where it ran within the girders. He had never apprehended any danger to himself or others from the use of the bridge.

He had often been between the high girders when a train had passed, and the bridge would scarcely vibrate at all – he never felt anything. He had been there when there had been a high wind and a train passing, but he had never felt anything like vibration or oscillation.

Murray had also never noticed, between hot weather in the summer and cold weather in the winter, any movement in the expansion joints at all. He therefore confirmed for the Commissioners the stability of the Tay Bridge in adverse weather conditions and in normal circumstances.

The Court of Inquiry

'For the faults of design Sir Thomas Bouch is entirely responsible. For those of construction, he is principally to blame. For the faults of maintenance he is also principally to blame, in having neglected to maintain such a watch over the structure as its character imperatively demanded.'

'The Board of Trade's chief inspector of railways observed that the subject of wind pressure never entered into the calculations that he himself made, and never had done.'

The Court of Inquiry concluded that the Tay Bridge had been badly designed, badly constructed and badly maintained, and that its downfall was due to inherent defects in the structure that must, sooner or later, have brought it down. For these defects, in design, construction and maintenance, Sir Thomas Bouch, the Commissioners concluded, was mainly to blame. For the faults of design he was entirely responsible. For those of construction, he was principally to blame in not having exercised the supervision over the work that would have enabled him to detect and apply a remedy to them.

For the faults of maintenance he was also principally, if not entirely, to blame, in having neglected to maintain such vigilance over the structure as its character imperatively demanded. Bouch overlooked allowances made for wind pressure in some other countries when he designed the Tay Bridge.

It is only fair at this point to set out Bouch's assessment of the causes of the fall of the Tay Bridge, which was summarised by the Court of Inquiry. The full exposition of the Court of Inquiry's account of Bouch's assessment can be found in Appendix 1.

Bouch stated it to be his opinion that the accident was occasioned by the overturning of the 2nd Class carriage and the van behind it by the force of the wind, and that they were canted over against the girder. The force of the blow given by these vehicles at the speed at which they were travelling was sufficient to destroy portions of the girders, and so occasioned the fall. However, the Court of Inquiry did not concur with this opinion. Nor did it consider that Bouch's view was supported by the evidence of the engineers who had been called on behalf of the railway company, Sir Thomas Bouch and the contractors.

The Court of Inquiry referred to the insufficiency of the cross-bracings and fastenings to sustain the force of the gale. A modern analysis using computer modelling has suggested that the bridge was under-designed for the wind, and was unlikely to have been able to resist force 10 gales, which were to be expected in the Firth of Tay [Martin and MacLeod, *The Tay Railway Bridge Disaster: A reappraisal based on modern analysis methods* (Proceedings, Institution of Civil Engineers, 1995)].

The Court of Inquiry was conducted by H. C. Rothery, William Yolland and William Barlow, the latter two both important Victorian civil engineers. It was asserted to the three Commissioners that Bouch should be judged by the state of current knowledge of wind pressures when he designed and built the bridge: in France an allowance of 55lb was made, and in the United States 50lb.

British engineers did not, however, agree on the due allowance to be made for wind pressure in the design of bridges. Bouch was building a bridge on somewhat new principles, and in a position where it would be peculiarly exposed to the action of westerly and south-westerly gales; not only did he make no allowance for wind pressure, but he actually built a bridge that was weaker, lighter, and with wider spans, than his previous works. To have designed and built a bridge that, if properly constructed in all respects, would only have borne a lateral pressure of from 60 to 70lb per square foot when a pressure of 40 to 50lb of wind was quite possible was a grave error of judgement, and gave far too low a margin of safety.

The Commissioners concluded that the bridge fell solely by the action of the wind, not due to any action by the train upon the girders of the bridge. Either the margin of safety was too low or the design defects too great, and in neither way could Bouch escape his responsibility.

The Court of Inquiry also considered the responsibility of the contractors, Messrs Hopkins, Gilkes & Co. They were not free from blame for having allowed grave irregularities to go on at the Wormit Foundry. Had competent persons been appointed to superintend the work there instead of its being left almost wholly in the hands of the foreman-moulder, there was little doubt that the columns would not have been sent out to the bridge with the serious defects that had been pointed out. They would also have taken care to see that the bolt-holes in the lugs and flanges of the 18-inch columns were cast truly cylindrical or, if that could not be done, they would have called the attention of the engineer or his assistants to the fact. But that was not done: the great object seemed to have been to get through the work with as little delay as possible, without seeing whether it was properly and carefully executed or not.

The Commissioners did not consider the North British Railway Company wholly free from blame for having allowed the trains to run through the high girders at a speed greatly in excess of that which General Hutchinson, the Board of Trade inspector, had suggested as the extreme limit. They ought to have known from the advertised times of running the trains that the speed over the bridge summit was more than 25mph, and they should not have allowed it until they had satisfied themselves, which they seemed to have taken no trouble to do, that that speed could be maintained without injury to the structure.

The last question posed by the Commissioners was whether the Board of Trade was also to blame for having allowed the bridge to be opened for passenger traffic as and when they did. By the Railway Regulation Act 1842, it was enacted that no new line of railway should be opened for passenger traffic until one month after notice of the company's intention to open it had been sent to the Board of Trade and until ten days after notice had been sent that it was complete and ready for inspection. No plans or drawings of the structure were required to be sent before the service of the notices, and, as a fact, the Board of Trade were seldom sent them before the ten days' notice had been served; frequently they were not received until afterwards. One of the Inspecting Officers of the Board of Trade had then to examine the plans and details, to inspect the railway, and to make his report. If a copy of the report and an order to postpone the opening were not sent to the railway authorities before the expiration of the ten days' notice, the company was permitted to open the line for passenger traffic without the sanction of the Board of Trade, whatever its then state and condition. Given the other duties of these inspectors, the examination could only be superficial.

In the case of the Tay Bridge, on receipt of the usual notices from the North British Railway Company of its intention to open the Tay Bridge for passenger traffic, Major General Hutchinson's inspection took place, as observed above, on 25, 26 and 27 February 1878. On the following 5 March, Hutchinson reported that his tests had shown him that there was 'no reason why the Board of Trade should object to the railway on the Tay Bridge being used for passenger traffic'. The fate of the bridge on 28 December of the following year showed that General Hutchinson had made a grave error of judgement concerning the bridge's capacity to withstand gales; indeed, he had made no calculations at all of the bridge's capacity to withstand wind pressure.

Hutchinson considered that his examination of the bridge had been sufficient to enable him to make his report. He had observed no symptoms of weakness that in his judgement had given any reason to doubt the stability of the structure, assuming it to be built of appropriate materials to an appropriate level of quality of workmanship.

General Hutchinson stated somewhat equivocally that the design was 'not unsatisfactory': there was nothing in the design, in his judgement, to warrant him objecting in any way to it. He declined to pledge himself to a general approval of the design; all that he would say was that he could see nothing in it that would justify him in taking the strong measure of withholding a certificate. So also with respect to the materials and the workmanship, he declined to say whether they were good, nor was it possible for him to do otherwise, seeing that the whole of the work was finished, and the defects, if any, covered up when he made his inspection. He admitted, very fairly, that his inspection had been only a superficial one, and that he could judge of the work only from its appearance externally.

The Commissioners observed that it was important to bear this in mind: there seemed to be an impression abroad that after a work had been inspected and passed by the Officers of the Board of Trade, the engineer and others by whom it was to be constructed were relieved from responsibility for any defects that might subsequently be discovered. The Commissioners considered that this could hardly be so. If the inspecting officers were to be held responsible for all defects both of design and of construction, not only should the plans be submitted to them for their approval before the work was commenced, but they ought, during its progress, to be allowed to exercise the same amount of supervision as the engineer and his assistants were supposed to do. Whether the country would be prepared to sanction any such interference with private enterprise, with the view of relieving those who were, and ought to be, primarily responsible, from the work of responsibility, might well be doubted. However, Parliament had not done so – all that the law required was that the officers of the Board of Trade should say not whether the design was good and the work constructed on the best principles, nor whether there were or were not any latent defects in it, but whether they might give any good reason why it should not be opened for passenger traffic.

The Commissioners, despite the disclaimers set out above, did note in connection with General Hutchinson's inspection that although he seemed to have tested the bridge sufficiently, indeed severely, for a vertical dead weight pressure, he made no allowance of any kind for wind pressure. This, he said, it was not the practice to do. That led to the question of how he could assess the stability of the bridge with no such calculations. As far as Hutchinson knew, wind pressure had never been taken into account.

General Hutchinson later considered, after what had come out in the course of the inquiry, that there could be no justification in future for disregarding altogether, as seemed to have been done, the effect of wind pressure on such a structure as the Tay Bridge. However, whether General Hutchinson was or was not to blame for having so done, Bouch was not relieved from his responsibility.

The Court of Inquiry's report concluded that there was little doubt that the bridge would be rebuilt. This was required by the interests of the large and thriving town of Dundee. If, however, it should be rebuilt with its narrow base, its cast-iron lugs, its conical bolt-holes, its unconnected L-girders, and with other numerous defects of the fallen bridge, and without adequate allowance being made for wind pressure, a very serious responsibility would rest on all concerned, and one that the country would not very readily pardon. While the blame for that might have been appropriately laid at Bouch's door, the Government's system of inspection also gravely failed the 60 men, women and children who lost their lives when the bridge went down on the night of 28 December 1879.

POSTSCRIPT

*'The Tay Bridge could never fall down. It was too much for
me to fathom, so I went about all day in a dream, and when I
was put to bed that night I only then realised what a terrible
disaster had happened. I did nothing else but cry all night at
the loss of one I loved so much, my dear sister Elizabeth.'*

All the passengers and the crew of four, every single person on the
doomed train, died in the Tay Bridge disaster. The bodies of 47 people
were recovered, and 13 were never found. Of those recovered, 43 were males
and four females. No bodies were recovered from inside the carriages or
engine; those bodies were presumably swept away by the force of the river.
Fourteen of the dead were buried at the Eastern Necropolis, Dundee, and six
at the Western Necropolis. Nineteen victims were buried elsewhere in Fife.

Who died in the fall of the Tay Bridge? It will probably never be known
exactly how many people died when the bridge went down. The Court of
Inquiry's report stated that there were in the train 74 or 75 people in all. The
very first report immediately after the disaster, from Robert Morris, the Station
Master at St Fort, had suggested that 300 passengers were on the train.

Different books have given different accounts of the numbers who died
that night. This is due to numbers being based either on tickets collected or
police records of the dead, which, given how soon after the fall of the bridge
the Court of Inquiry took place, could hardly have been available to the
Court. Forty-four bodies were not recovered until after the Court of Inquiry
had finished taking evidence, and a further 13 were never recovered.

Dates (1880)	No of bodies recovered
January	31
February	8
March	2
April	5
Not recovered	13
Not known	1
Total	60

Swinfen (see the Bibliography) says that 75 passengers and crew were lost, 'derived from a count of the tickets collected at St Fort station'. Peter Lewis says that 'over 80' lives were lost, but gives no source for this statement.

The following list of 60 dead passengers and crew is drawn from Murray Nicoll, Claire Nicoll and Grant Buttars's *Victims of the Tay Bridge Disaster 1879* (Dundee, 2005), and is based on police records. The list includes one extra name, James Paton, who is listed by Swinfen but not Nicoll et al. (NR indicates that the body was not recovered.)

Name and age	Occupation	Address	Date body recovered
Anderson, Joseph Low (21)	Compositor	Dundee	23.4.80
Annan, Thomas Ross (20)	Iron turner	Dundee	11.4.80
Bain, Archibald (26)	Farmer	Balgay	8.1.80
Bain, Jessie (22)	Farmer's daughter (sister of Archibald Bain)	Balgay	18.2.80
Beynon, William Henry (39)	Photographer	Cheltenham	7.2.80
Brown, Elizabeth Hendry (14)	Tobacco spinner (travelling with her grandmother, Elizabeth Mann)	Dundee	NR
Cheape, Euphemia (51)	Domestic servant	Lochee	NR
Crichton, James (22)	Ploughman	Mains of Fintry	6.1.80
Cruickshanks, Ann (54)	Domestic servant	Edinburgh	29.12.80
Culross, Robert (28)	Carpenter	Tayport	13.3.80
Cunningham, David (20)	Mason	Dundee	10.1.80
Davidson, Thomas (28)	Ploughman	Linlathen	8.1.80
Easton, Mary Marion (53)	Widow	Aberdeen	NR
Fowlis, Robert Dewar (21)	Mason	Lochee	12.1.80
Graham, David (37)	Teacher	Stirling	NR
Hamilton, John (32)	Grocer	Dundee	NR
Henderson, James Foster (22)	Labourer	Dundee	8.1.80
Jack, William (23)	Grocer	Scoonie, Fife	6.1.80
Jobson, David (39)	Oil, colour merchant	Dundee	17.2.80
Johnston, David (24)	Railway guard (not on duty)	Edinburgh	15.1.80
Johnston, George (25)	Mechanic (travelling with his fiancée, Eliza Smart)	Dundee	8.1.80
Kinnear, Margaret (17)	Domestic servant	Dundee	14.4.80
Lawson, John (25)	Plasterer	Dundee	10.1.80
Leslie, James (22)	Clerk	Dundee	6.1.80
Mann, Elizabeth (62)	Not recorded (travelling with her granddaughter, Elizabeth Brown)	Forfar	NR
Marshall, John (24)	Loco fireman (on duty)	Dundee	7.1.80

McBeth, David (44)	Guard (on duty)	Dundee	13.1.80
McDonald, David (11)	Schoolboy (son of William McDonald)	Dundee	9.1.80
McDonald, William (41)	Saw miller (father of David McDonald)	Dundee	7.1.80
McIntosh, George (48)	Goods guard	Dundee	16.2.80
Miller, James (26)	Flax dresser	Dysart	7.1.80
Milne, Elizabeth (21)	Dressmaker	Newburgh	NR
Mitchell, David (37)	Loco driver (on duty)	Dundee	1.3.80
Murdoch, James (21)	Engineer	Dundee	6.2.80
Murray, Donald (49)	Mail guard (on duty)	Dundee	NR
Neish, David (37)	Teacher (father of Isabella Neish)	Dundee	7.1.80
Neish, Isabella Mary (5)	Daughter of David Neish	Dundee	27.1.80
Nelson, William (31)	Machine fitter	Gateshead	NR
Ness, George (21)	Loco fireman (not on duty)	Tayport	13.1.80
Ness, Walter (24)	Saddler	Dundee	7.1.80
Nicoll, Elizabeth (24)	Not recorded	Dundee	NR
Paton, James (42)	Mechanic	Edinburgh	Not known
Peebles, James (15)	Apprentice grocer	Newport, Fife	11.4.80
Peebles, William (38)	Land steward	Inverness	9.1.80
Robertson, Alexander (23)	Labourer (brother of William Robertson)	Dundee	8.1.80
Robertson, William (21)	Gasworks fireman (brother of Alexander Robertson)	Dundee	27.4.80
Salmond, Peter Greig (43)	Blacksmith	Dundee	7.2.80
Scott, David (26)	Goods guard	Dundee	NR
Scott, John (30)	Seaman, *Halcyon*, Hartlepool	Baltimore	23.2.80
Sharp, John (35)	Joiner	Dundee	7.1.80
Smart, Eliza (22)	Table maid (travelling with her fiancé, George Johnston)	Dundee	NR
Spence, Annie (21)	Weaver	Dundee	NR
Syme, Robert Frederick (22)	Clerk, Royal Hotel	Dundee	11.1.80
Taylor, George (25)	Mason/cutter	Dundee	11.3.80
Threlfell, William (18)	Confectioner	Dundee	7.1.80
Veitch, William (18)	Cabinet-maker	Dundee	13.1.80
Watson, David (18)	Commission agent	Dundee	7.1.80
Watson, David Livie (9)	Schoolboy (son of Robert Watson, brother of Robert)	Dundee	16.1.80
Watson, Robert (6)	Schoolboy (son of Robert Watson, brother of David)	Dundee	9.1.80
Watson, Robert (34)	Moulder (father of David and Robert Watson)	Dundee	6.1.80

The bare statistics of numbers of people lost and bodies recovered or not recovered mask the human tragedy. Among the passengers were seven children, all of whom were in the second 3rd Class carriage. For example, David Neish, a 37-year-old teacher who lived at 51 Cupar Street, Dundee, died with his 5-year-old daughter, Isabella. She was a fair-haired girl, wearing a black satin dress and a black cloth jacket, her dress trimmed with feathers. She had kid-dressed shoes and a small white shawl around her neck. Her father's body was recovered on 7 January 1880, but his little daughter was not recovered until 27 January. Both bodies were identified by Neish's brother-in-law, but his wife only identified her young daughter. It is easy to conceive the anguish she must have been going through that prevented her from identifying her husband only just over a week after her loved ones had been lost.

It is invidious to rank the depths of particular tragedies, but it is difficult to conceive the depth of Mary Watson's: she lost her husband and two sons aged 9 and 6 when the bridge went down. The family lived at 12 Lawrence Street, Dundee. Mary recovered her menfolk on 6, 9 and 16 January, and they were buried side by side in the Eastern Necropolis in Dundee, where a total of 14 of the victims were buried. She presented £1 to the crew of the boat who had found her loved ones, as a mark of respect.

George Johnston, a 25-year-old mechanic from Victoria Road, Dundee, died with his 22-year-old fiancée, Eliza Smart. She was identified by a neighbour from Perth Road in Dundee, while her fiancé was identified by his father.

Yet another tragedy was that which befell Ann Mann, who lived at Arbroath Road in Dundee. She was travelling with her 14-year-old granddaughter Elizabeth Brown, a tobacco spinner. Elizabeth was 5ft 1in tall, red-haired and inclined to freckles. Both deaths were notified to Elizabeth's mother, Jane, but neither body was ever recovered. Her other granddaughter recounted that after having slept heavily that night she was woken up by the sound of people crying. On leaving her bedroom, she found her mother, uncle and elder brother in a terrible state of distress. Her mother told her, in a broken voice, 'You will never see your grandmother again: everybody on the train has been drowned.' Elizabeth Brown is mentioned on a stone at the Eastern Necropolis, Dundee.

Other people related to each other who died included Archibald Bain and his sister Jessie, who had been visiting their uncle in Cupar. Their bodies were identified by their father; they were only 26 and 22 years of age. They were buried side by side in the Western Cemetery in Dundee.

The oldest of the children who lost their lives was Margaret Kinnear, a 17-

year-old domestic servant from Dundee, whose body was not recovered until 14 April 1880, some three and a half months after the disaster. Her body was identified by Robert Lee, who lived at the same address. She was a domestic servant and had been wearing a striped petticoat, a dark green dress, a jacket trimmed with dark fur, a black straw hat and suede boots.

David McDonald was 11 years old, and lived in Dundee. He was travelling with his father, William, a 41-year-old saw miller from Blackness Road, Dundee. David's body was recovered on 9 January 1880 and was identified by his uncle; he was buried in the Eastern Necropolis, Dundee. David was small for his age, with dark hair and a dark complexion, and his body was found while his father's funeral service was taking place at the Eastern Necropolis in Dundee.

James Peebles had just begun work at Newport, Fife, as an apprentice grocer, at the age of 15. Neither of his parents was on the train. He had five shillings and sixpence cash in his pocket. His body was recovered on 11 April 1880 at Tayport Harbour, and he was buried at Kilmany Kirkyard, Fife.

A number of relatives had the sad task of recovering what their loved ones had been carrying that night. William Threlfell's mother, Euphemia, collected her son's handkerchief and hymn book. Her son was only 18, and his body was found in the middle of the Tay beside the training ship *Mars* a week after the bridge had gone down.

Obviously the loss of relatives left many grieving people, and one such case is illustrated by the following. Nicoll, Nicoll and Butters cite the following reminiscence of the disaster, although they do not link it to a specific victim:

> 'For a while I could not grasp what I had been told. The Tay Bridge could never fall down. It was too much for me to fathom, so I went about all day in a dream, and when I was put to bed that night I only then realised what a terrible disaster had happened. I did nothing else but cry all night at the loss of one I loved so much, my dear sister Elizabeth'.

The force of the 'sheet of foam' swept many bodies away from the scene of the disaster and, as has been remarked, 13 of the 60 passengers were never recovered. The bodies found at the greatest distance from the Tay Bridge were those of Robert Culross and George Taylor. Robert Culross's body was found on 13 March 1880 2 miles east of Monifieth. George Taylor's body was found on 11 March 2 miles east of Tayport. Robert Culross was a 28-year-old carpenter, a single man, from Tayport; he had no dependents or family. George Taylor was a 35-year-old man who lived at 56 Union Street in Dundee; his profession is not recorded. The grisly task of identifying his body two and a half months after the bridge had gone down fell to his widowed mother, with whom he was still living.

At the end of February a memorial service was held in Dundee's Taybridge station, led by a United Reformed minister. A large number of people attended.

Thomas Bouch died on 30 October 1880, only four months after the Court of Inquiry's report had been published. He was 58 years old. The designer of the world's longest bridge had borne the whole blame of the Court of Inquiry into why the bridge had gone down. None of the blame was attached to the Board of Trade inspector who had passed the bridge as adequate for its purpose. As we have seen, the Court of Inquiry had concluded that the bridge had been badly designed, for which Thomas Bouch was blamed; it had been badly built, for which Thomas Bouch was blamed; and it had been badly maintained, for which Thomas Bouch was also blamed.

The Select Committee on the Bill to build the Tay Bridge had asked Sir Thomas Bouch very little about wind pressure, and the bridge's capacity to withstand it. Bouch told the Committee that William Barlow and Dr Pole (FRS, who in conjunction with Allan Stewart supplied information required of the North British Railway Company by the Court of Inquiry) were not satisfied with their own judgement upon the question of wind pressure and it was they who consulted the Astronomer Royal. Bouch could therefore assert to the Select Committee that in the design, being one of extraordinary magnitude, every possible precaution had been taken to get the opinion of the best talent in the country as to its sufficiency in every respect.

One of the members of the Court of Inquiry that had been so critical of Sir Thomas Bouch, the engineer William Barlow, was employed to engineer the replacement bridge over the River Tay.

Isambard Kingdom Brunel, arguably the greatest of Victorian railway engineers, had told his Board of directors that he regarded it as his duty as an engineer 'to seek the perfection of the surface on which the carriages are to run as the greatest and ultimate desideratum'. The fate of the Tay Bridge showed that Sir Thomas Bouch, through a conjunction of mischances for many of which he was not responsible, had not achieved the perfection Brunel regarded as the principal responsibility of any civil engineer when building a railway.

The 4-4-0 tender engine, No 224, survived the fall of the Tay Bridge. Dredged from the river, it was repaired and put back to work. Ghoulishly, it was subsequently nicknamed 'The Diver', and remained in service until 1917, 37 years after the fall of the Tay Bridge. Those carriages that were brought up proved to be beyond further use, but fragments of their wooden bodies were used to make mementoes of the disaster.

The little that remained of Bouch's stunning vision was thus 'The Diver', the broken stumps in the River Tay, and some wooden walking sticks and other carved souvenirs.

APPENDIX 1
THE COURT OF INQUIRY
REPORT

(i) The course of the inquiry

The inquiry was set up under the Regulation of Railways Act 1871 to examine the causes and the circumstances attending the fall of the Tay Bridge. The inquiry was opened on Saturday 3 January, only a few days after the bridge had gone down. The last witness was heard on 6 January. At this point the bridge was visited by the Commissioners.

Mr Henry Law, a member of the Institution of Civil Engineers, was given directions to make a minute and careful examination of the bridge and to report fully on the probable cause of the accident. Photographs of the piers, of portions of the fallen girders and permanent way and of the remains of the engine and carriages were ordered to be prepared.

While this was under way, further witnesses were examined, mainly with reference to alleged defects of workmanship and inferior quality of materials used in the bridge; and also as to the speed at which the trains crossed it.

The inquiry was resumed at Westminster on Monday 19 April 1880, and between that day and Saturday 8 May, when it was brought to a close, a large number of witnesses were examined. On this occasion, Sir Thomas Bouch, the engineer, and Messrs Hopkins, Gilkes & Co, the contractors, appeared by separate counsel.

A contract to build the bridge was made on 1 May 1871 and entered into with Messrs de Bergue & Co to undertake the work. In consequence of the illness of Mr Charles de Bergue, the leading partner in the contractor's firm, and his inability to attend to business, the contract was transferred on 26 June 1874 to Messrs Hopkins, Gilkes & Co of Middlesbrough to complete the work. The new contractors took over from Messrs de Bergue the whole of the existing staff and plant, as well as a foundry that had been erected at

Wormit, near the southern end of the bridge, where a large portion of the castings required for the works were made.

The bridge was designed by Sir Thomas Bouch, who also supervised its construction. He was subsequently charged by the North British Railway Company with its maintenance.

(ii) Imperfection of workmanship and fitting

In regard to the imperfection of the workmanship and fitting, it appears that as the substitution of iron for brick piers in this part of the work was made after the contract was let, there are no clauses in the specification describing the class of workmanship to be employed in them.

The stipulation in the general specification, which requires all the holes in the flanges of the columns to be drilled, was not carried out in this part of the work as regards the holes in the flanges of the 18-inch columns; the holes in the lugs on the columns were all cast and left conical, instead of being drilled, thus causing the pins to have unequal bearings. Some of the sling-plates, which were made or altered at the works, were roughly formed.

Imperfection of workmanship was also found in the bolt-holes of the struts, and as the struts did not abut against the columns, as in our opinion they ought to have done, their action in these cases depended on the friction or resistance to movement made by bolting the channel-irons tightly together, and bearing hard against the lugs.

The columns after the accident were found in some instances to be of unequal thickness, and to have other defects of casting, and it was probably due to the sluggish character of the metal and the manner in which the columns were cast, that the castings of the lugs did not always turn out sound, as out of 14 tie-bars attached to lugs, tested in London, four showed unsoundness to a greater or lesser extent at the lugs.

It is stated in evidence that, in some cases where lugs had turned out imperfect in casting, other lugs or portions of lugs were added by a process termed 'burning-on'. This is admitted to have been done; but it is denied that any columns so treated were used in the permanent structure, and, although a large number of broken lugs are visible in the ruins of the fallen bridge, none were found during Mr Law's examination, nor have been otherwise brought to our notice, which appear to have been subjected to this most objectionable and dangerous process.

(iii) Official inspection of the bridge

The bridge was inspected by General Hutchinson on 25, 26 and 27 February 1878, at which time it was all finished and painted. During this inspection he subjected the bride to various tests, and among others he caused six locomotives coupled together, each weighing 73 tons, to pass over the bridge at a speed of 40 miles per hour. The behaviour of the bridge under these tests appears to have been satisfactory, there having been only a moderate deflection in the girders, a small degree of tremor, and no indication of looseness in the cross-bracing.

On 5 March he reported that he saw 'no reason why the Board of Trade should object' to the bridge being used for passenger traffic; but that it would 'not be desirable that trains should run over the bridge at a high rate of speed', and suggested '25 miles per hour as a limit, which should not be exceeded', adding that 'very careful attention will be required to ascertain from time to time that no scouring action is taking place in the foundations', and that he should wish, if possible, to have an opportunity of 'observing the effects of a high wind when a train of carriages is running over the bridge'. Some delay occurred in opening the bridge, owing to the approaches on either side not being completed, but on the 1st day of June 1878 it was open for passenger traffic, and from that time trains continued to run regularly across it until the evening of 28 December last, on which date what we are about to describe occurred.

(iv) Circumstances attending accident

The train previous to that which fell with the bridge left Tayport about 5.50pm, and crossed the bridge about 6.05pm. The engine driver did not notice anything unusual in the travelling of this train, but the guard, Shand, and two men who were with him, saw sparks of fire coming from the wheels of the carriages. Shand put on this brake, and showed his red light, but it was not seen by the driver; he also examined his train at the Dundee station, but finding nothing wrong made no report.

The train from Edinburgh that fell with the bridge arrived in due course at St Fort station, and there the tickets of the passengers for Dundee were as usual collected. We were told by the ticket collectors that there were at that time in the train 57 passengers for Dundee, five or six for Broughty Ferry, five for Newport, two season ticket holders, the driver, stoker, and guard of the train, and two other guards, making 74 or 75 persons altogether. The tickets having been collected, the train proceeded on its course, leaving St Fort station at 7.08pm, and on approaching the cabin that stands at the southern end of the bridge the speed was slackened to about 3 or 4 miles per hour to enable the engine driver to take the baton or train staff without which he is not allowed to cross the bridge. On receiving the baton, steam was again turned on, and the train passed onto the bridge, upon which the signalman, Thomas Barclay, signalled to the north cabin signalman the time according to the entry in his book, being exactly 13 minutes after 7 o'clock. It was then blowing a strong gale from about WSW, and therefore almost directly across the bridge; there was a full moon, but it was quite dark, owing to the face of the moon being obscured by clouds. It seems that a surfaceman in the employment of the North British Railway Company, named John Watt, had gone to keep Barclay company and was in the cabin when the train passed; and while Barclay was attending to his duties, entering the time in his book, and making up the stove fire, Watt was watching the train through the window in the cabin door, which looks north along the line. According to Watt, when the train had got about 200 yards from the cabin he observed sparks flying from the wheels; and when they had continued about three minutes, there was a sudden bright flash of light, and in an instant there was total darkness, the tail-lamps of the train, the sparks, and flash of light, he said, disappearing at the same instant.

The portion of the bridge that fell consisted of three sets of continuous girders, covering respectively five spans, four spans, and four spans, making 13 spans altogether.

These continuous girders rested on rollers on all their piers except one near the centre of each set, and to these central piers they were fixed. In the accident which took place, the girders turned over and fell on their sides, each girder becoming slightly curved, the centre portion being farthest from the piers, and the ends curving towards the piers, some irregularities showing in the curve at the first fallen pier from the south end.

The train was found partly in the fourth and partly in the fifth spans from the south end, so that, although it had travelled some distance along the first set of continuous girders, it never reached the northern extremity. The engine and tender were found lying on their sides on the eastern girders. The train consisted (counting from the engine) of one 3rd Class, one 1st Class, two 3rd Class, one 2nd Class and the guard's van. The 2nd Class carriage and the guard's van had their bodies and all the upper portions entirely destroyed; their lower frames were greatly damaged, and the axles of these vehicles as well as those of all the other carriages were bent.

The throttle-valve of the engine was full open, and the reversing lever standing in the sixth notch from full forward gear, or in the third notch from the centre. The train was partly fitted with the Westinghouse brake, but there was no appearance of it having been put on, and the conclusion to be drawn from these facts is that neither the driver nor fireman had any warning of the accident which took place.

(v) Wind pressure

It appears in the evidence that about the time Sir T. Bouch considered the altered designs of the Tay Bridge, he had been preparing plans for a bridge over the Firth of Forth for another company. This bridge being of unprecedented magnitude as regards its spans, and several railway companies being interested in its construction, other engineers, viz, Sir J. Hawkshaw, Mr Bidder, Mr T. Harrison and Mr Barlow, were consulted, and it was remitted to Mr Barlow and Dr Pole to carry out the detailed investigation of the design. It further appears that these gentlemen, not being satisfied with their own judgement on the question of wind pressure, consulted the Astronomer Royal, who put his opinion in writing in a letter from which the following is an extract:

'We know that upon very limited surfaces, and for very limited times, the pressure of the wind does amount sometimes to 40lb per square foot, or, in Scotland, probably to more. So far as I am aware, our positive knowledge, as derived from instrumental record, goes no further; but in studying the registers it is impossible not to see that these high pressures are momentary, and it seems most probable that they arise from some irregular whirlings of the air which extend to no great distance, I should say certainly to no distance comparable to the dimensions of the proposed bridge, and I think that the fairest estimate of the pressure on the entire bridge would be formed by taking the mean of the recorded pressures at one point of space for a moderate extent of time as representing the mean pressures on a moderate extent of space at one instant of time. Adopting this consideration, I think we may say that the greatest wind pressure to which a plain surface like that of the bridge will be subjected in its whole extent is 10lb per square foot.'

Furnished with this opinion, Messrs Barlow and Pole report:

'We entirely concur in this opinion, which we consider highly authoritative and valuable, and we may therefore safely adopt 10lb per square foot as the side pressure due to the wind for which Mr Bouch has to provide. We may now describe the means which Mr Bouch has adopted to provide against this side pressure: the side surface of each span exposed to the wind (but making allowance for some parts which may be assumed to bear directly on the piers) is given by Mr Stewart at about 14,000 superficial feet. This is for one surface only, ie the one first exposed to the wind; but behind this there are three similar surfaces, one about 15 feet away, the second about 120 feet away, and the third about 135 feet away. The wind must rush past these after passing the first one; and although each will be, no doubt, to a certain extent in shelter from those in front of it, we cannot suppose that they will be free from the wind's action. Possibly it would be a fair estimate to double the surface of the front face, but as an outside estimate we have taken three times or 42,000. To this has been added 8,000 feet for two trains which may be on the bridge, giving 50,000 square feet of surface exposed to the horizontal action of the wind. Allowing, therefore, 10lb per square foot, we get a force of about 225 tons.'

Their conclusions, so arrived at, were adopted in the report signed by Sir J. Hawkshaw, Mr Bidder, Mr T. Harrison and Mr Barlow.

Sir T. Bouch states that this report influenced his mind and that, in consequence, he did not think it necessary to make any special provision for wind pressure in the Tay Bridge.

But we think he must have misunderstood the nature of that report, for, as it pointed out that the pressures in gusts of wind amounted to 40lb or more, it was obviously necessary to provide for the pressures so arising in each of the spans of the Tay Bridge, and although the limited area of these gusts is described as not being at all comparable to that of the Forth Bridge of 1,600 feet span, yet they might in effect be equal to the whole area in the 245-feet spans of the Tay Bridge, and their operation might take place upon any of the spans.

It must not be understood, however, that we express an opinion as to the sufficiency of a provision for only 10lb of wind pressure in a large span of 1,600 feet. It may represent an amount of force which, as applied to the whole surface, would rarely be exceeded, but after hearing the evidence given at this inquiry it occurs to us as possible that two or more gusts might act simultaneously on such a large span, or there might be a wind gust of unusual width.

(vi) Evidence on wind pressure

With a view to obtain information on the subject of wind pressure from the most authentic sources, we applied to the Astronomer Royal, to Professor Stokes, and Mr R. H. Scott, the secretary to the Meteorological Council, and from the evidence given by these gentlemen we learn the following particulars.

It appears that the term 'wind pressure', as now usually employed, means the force produced by the wind when acting against and at right-angles to a flat plate or disc; and it is expressed in pounds per square foot. It can be arrived at directly by the instrument known as Osler's anemometer, which consists of a flat plate or board acting against a spring with a recording apparatus, which exhibits the degrees of compression produced on the spring by the action of the wind, or it can be deduced approximately from the 'standard pressure, by which term is meant the height at which a column of fluid is maintained or supported by wind pressure, or it can be deduced approximately from the velocity of the wind, due allowance being made for the height of the barometer and thermometer and the hydrometrical state of the air at the time, and its amount varies nearly as the surface of the plate exposed to the wind's action.

The relation between the pressure as obtained from a plate and the standard pressure can only be ascertained by experiments, and different experimenters have assigned differed values to it. Dr Hutton makes the relation 1.4; others have made it as high as 2, but it is now considered to be 1.8.

The instrument used for measuring the velocity of the wind is the revolving cup instrument known as Robinson's anemometer. It is considered that a constant ratio exists between the velocity of the wind and the cups actuated by the wind. That ratio was supposed to be 3, but recently carefully conducted experiments by Dr Robinson place it at 2.28. More recent experiments indicate 2.4 as the ratio. As a general average result, it is considered that wind with a velocity of 20mph produces a standard pressure of 1lb, or 1.8lb per foot pressure on a flat board, and that the pressure increases as the square of the velocity.

The diagram produced by the cup anemometer, as the apparatus is now arranged, does not enable the velocity in short periods of time to be ascertained with certainty; hence it is not possible to determine by its means the velocity in gusts of wind.

Osler's anemometer appears to afford the most direct and reliable means of ascertaining wind pressure on a flat surface.

The highest record arrived at by this instrument was a pressure of 90lb, which occurred on 9 March 1872 at Bidstone. It is stated that the instrument was graduated only up to 40lb, but the marker was driven beyond to a distance estimated to represent about 90lb. Excepting this one result, the greatest pressure actually recorded is 50lb, which occurred in Calcutta, but there are numerous examples of pressures of 40lb, and between 40 and 50lb.

Professor Stoke states that the position of the anemometer may materially affect the velocity and pressures recorded by it. It may be so placed as to have partial shelter, in which case the recorded result is too small, or it may be placed in the draught passing round some obstruction to windward of it, in which case the record is too high.

Pressures deduced from wind velocities require to be received with great caution: first, because there is doubt as to the accuracy of the estimated wind velocity; secondly, because there is a further doubt as to the relation between velocity and pressure; and thirdly, because the pressure is supposed to vary as the square of the velocity, so that any error in the estimated velocity becomes greatly exaggerated when turned into pressure.

Some instances of railway carriages being upset by wind are clearly established in France, India and America, and one occurred in this country on the Chester & Holyhead line in 1868.

The pressure required to overturn railway carriages may be taken to vary between 28 and 40lb per square foot. A distinction is made between pressures of gusts of wind and those extraordinary destructive effects that arise from cyclonic faction or tornadoes, one of which is cited as having occurred at Walmer, causing great destruction as it passed along over a width varying from 450 to 700 feet, but it is not known whether the pressure was equal throughout the width at the same instance of time.

Another cyclone of somewhat similar character occurred in the Isle of Wight in November 1877.

The movement of the recording paper as generally used with Osler's anemometer is so slow that wind gusts have the appearance of being absolutely momentary in their action, but by causing the paper to travel quicker and by other observations, the duration of wind gusts is found sometimes to exceed half a minute, though they are generally of less duration.

As against the evidence which tends to show high wind pressure there are many facts recorded in Mr Baker's evidence of structures continuing to stand though unable to bear high pressures. Smallness of height or partial shelter may account for such cases, but as regards engineering structures placed high above the ground or otherwise in exposed positions there appears to be absolute necessity to provide for large wind pressures.

(vii) Special provision for wind not always required

In the great majority of railway structures, namely, those made in brickwork and masonry, as well as iron bridges of moderate height and span, special provision is not required for wind pressure, because the weight and lateral strength imparted to such structures, in providing for the strains due to dead weight and load, is more than sufficient to meet any lateral wind pressures that can arise. Also, in girders up to considerable spans, the lateral stiffness given to them to resist the tendency to oscillation produced by moving loads at high speeds is generally sufficient to meet the requirements of wind pressures; and the evidence of Sir Thomas Bouch implies that, having provided amply for dead weight and moving loads in the Tay Bridge, he did not consider it necessary to make special provision against wind pressure.

(viii) Calculations of strength

The report of Dr Pole and Mr Stewart, who were engaged in this inquiry for Sir T. Bouch, after referring to the knowledge possessed at the time of designing these piers, states as follows:

> 'For these reasons, in designing the bridge, a maximum wind pressure was assumed acting over the surface of a span and pier equal to about 20lb per square foot (being more than double what Smeaton allowed for a very high wind), and the dimensions were calculated for this pressure, with the usual margin of safety.'

It appears that Dr Pole and Mr Stewart were wrongly informed on this subject, as Sir T. Bouch stated that he did not make any special provision for wind pressure.

The calculations of the action of wind pressure on open-work girders necessarily involve some assumptions. In those made by Dr Pole and Mr Stewart, and also by Mr Law (who was employed by the Court), it is assumed that the pressures per unit of surface acting upon the leeward girder, so far as it is exposed to the wind, were one half those acting on the windward girder. And on this assumption, Dr Pole and Mr Stewart calculate that, with a wind pressure of 20lb, the stress on the minimum section of the wind-ties running east and west at the lowest division of the pier would be:

With no train upon the bridge	5.21 tons per inch
With light passenger train over one pier	6.79 tons per inch

It is to be observed that in making this calculation Messrs Pole and Stewart have not considered the ties as performing the whole duty of resisting the wind, but they have deducted from 20 to 25% of the total force, which they consider to be the resistance the columns would offer to an amount of bending corresponding to the lateral motion assumed. The resistance to bending is without doubt an element contributing to the strength, so far as it can be relied upon; but having regard to the fact that these piers were composed of seven tiers of columns connected together by bolts and nuts, and that the base-plates to which they were fastened at the top of the masonry were only held down at their bases by bolts passing through two courses of stone, we think that a reduction of 20 or 25% on account of the resistance of such columns to bending not admissible, and that, as a matter of ordinary precaution, the calculation ought not to be so treated. But as this great reduction has been made in the strength of the ties, no further deduction in the usual margin of safety (or the factor of 4) should on any account be permitted.

The minimum sectional area of the ties is stated in that report to be 1.69 inches, and the total stress on the ties would therefore be:

With no train	5.21 times 1.69 = 8.80 tons
With train over pier	6.79 times 1.69 = 11.47 tons

If these stresses be multiplied by four, the usual factor of safety, the ultimate strength required in the ties would, under the assumed conditions, be:

With no train	8.80 times 4 = 35.20 tons
With train over pier	11.47 times four = 45.88 tons

The ultimate strength given to these ties should not, therefore, have been less than 45.88 tons, under the conditions assumed. But the mean ultimate strength of six of the ties tested by Mr Kirkcaldy without the lugs was only 25.6 tons, and the mean strength of 14 tie-bars tested with the lugs was 24.1 tons, of which six broke with less than 22 tons, four of the latter giving way at unsound lugs, and two of them breaking with less than 21 tons.

The experiments were made on ties and lugs taken from the ruins, but no injury was apparent on them from that cause, and we think the weakness found in them was due to causes to which we will now refer.

(ix) Cross-bracing

The tensile strength of the wrought-iron used in the ties was proved by Mr Kirkaldy's experiments to be 20 tons to the inch, and, the minimal section area of the tie-bars as measured being 1.625 inches, they ought to have carried 32.5 tons; but the bearing surface of the pin was much less than the minimum sectional area, and, the pin being placed very near the extremity of the bar, it was not capable of developing the whole strength of the metal, which yielded by tearing or fracture at the pin-hole.

Again, as regards the cast-iron lugs, the tensile strength of the metal obtained from the average of 14 specimens cut out of broken cast-iron columns was 9.1 tons per square inch, the weakest being 8.1 tons per square inch. Fourteen cast-iron lugs to which the tie-bars were attached, and which formed portions of the diagonal cross-bracing between the columns, were tested in London. These tests were made by strains applied in the same direction as the lugs would be subjected to on the piers. Of these, ten were found to be sound castings, and four unsound. Of the sound castings, the strongest bore less than 3 tons per square inch before breaking, the average 2.8 tons per square inch, and the weakest 2.44 tons per square inch before they broke.

We believe this great apparent reduction of strength in the cast-iron is attributable to the nature of the fastenings, which caused the stress to be brought on the edges or outer sides of the lugs instead of acting fairly on them. And we wish to direct attention especially to these results, because the employment of wrought-iron ties bolted to cast-iron lugs is a mode of contraction frequently employed in other structures, and the deficiency of strength arising from it is not, we think, generally known.

As a question of ultimate strength, it may be urged that, if the weakest ties bore nearly 21 tons, the viaduct ought to have been able to resist 35lb per square foot of wind pressure, because, according to the calculations of Messrs Pole and Stewart, 35lb of pressure would have been required to have produced that strain. But Messrs Pole and Stewart's calculation is based upon the assumption that the columns and their connecting bolts bear 20 or 25% of the wind pressure, leaving only 75% or 80% to be carried by the ties; it also assumes that all the ties are equally tightened up, that the columns are in their correct position, and that every part or member of the pier is performing its exact proportion of duty.

These are conditions that can only exist within the elastic limits of the materials, and the elastic limit of iron in tension is somewhere about half its ultimate strength; that limit once passed, it is impossible to say what would be the relation between the strains in the different members of which the pier was composed.

Mr Kirkaldy's experiments show that the stretching or elongation of the ties, when tested with their fastenings, was greatly in excess of that due to the elastic action of that material; a result attributable to the small bearing surfaces of the pins, gibs and cotters, and to the conical holes in the lugs.

In considering the construction of these piers, it is further to be observed that any considerable stretching of the diagonal bracing, and consequent departure of the columns from the vertical, was a derangement or distortion, which it was especially important to avoid because such a movement could not take place without causing an unequal bearing at the bases or at the joints of the columns where it occurred, and might either result in fracture of the flanges or of the connecting bolts.

And if, from this or any other cause, one of the outer columns became fractured so as to be incapable of bearing weight, the L-shaped box girder would have been deprived of the support necessary to sustain the main girder pressing upon it. The liability to accident from this cause is a direct consequence of the peculiar construction adopted in these piers.

The hexagonal form given to the pier had also the effect of throwing the main duty of resisting wind pressure upon the cross-bracing between the inner 15-inch columns. The cross-bracing on the four oblique planes formed between the 18-inch and 15-inch columns and placed on those planes at an unfavourable vertical angle, contributed proportionately much less resistance to lateral pressure.

Before leaving the subject of the cross-bracing, we think it right to point out that this part of the structure forms a comparatively small item in the quantity of metal and consequent cost of the bridge. The weight of the cross-bracing in one of the high piers was stated approximately at 5 tons, the total weight of iron in the piers being 78 tons, and it will be seen from the return of the quantities of iron-work used by the contractors that out of a total quantity of iron of 10,518 tons, only 413 tons is classed under the head of 'bracing'.

It would appear, therefore, that a great increase of strength might have been given to the cross-bracing on which so much depends in resisting wind pressure without adding a large percentage to the cost of the bridge.

The wind force required to overturn the piers as a whole, assuming that there were no holding-down bolts, was estimated as:

	No train on bridge	With train on bridge
Mr Law	36.38lb per sq ft	34.33lb per sq ft
Messrs Pole and Stewart	37.40lb per sq ft	34.44lb per sq ft

In these estimates it is, of course, assumed that the cross-bracing and other parts are of adequate strength.

The holding-down bolts passed through two courses of stone, and if the effect of the additional weight thus brought into operation be taken into account, together with a fair allowance for the tenacity of the cement, the stability as against overturning would have been sufficient to resist 40lb of wind, if the cross-bracing had been made strong enough to resist that pressure.

An opinion has been frequently expressed that the bases of the piers were too narrow, and it is clear that the requisite stability could have been obtained more readily if the bridge had been made for a double instead of a single line of railway; but with iron-work and bracing of sufficient strength in all their parts, held down by strong bolts bedded down deep in the solid mass of the piers, there is no doubt that the caissons are wide enough, to permit of piers being constructed adequate to perform all the duty required.

(x) Fall of the bridge

There is no absolute knowledge of the mode in which the structure broke down; the evidence of persons who happened to be looking at the bridge at the time agrees in describing lights falling into the river, and that these appearances lasted only a few seconds. But the evidence is not sufficiently clear and definite to determine by it which portion of the bridge fell first.

It is observable in the ruins of the bridge that the columns have for the most part separated where they had been bolted to the base pieces; in two piers, the separation has taken place higher up the pier, one being at the first and the other at the second tier of columns.

At piers Nos 33 and 37, which were at the disconnected ends of the girders, the masonry is considerably disturbed and the stonework has been partly torn up where it was fastened to the base-pieces by the holding-down bolts; this effect is especially observable on the windward sides of these piers. The fractures of the cross-bracing are in almost every instance at the lugs.

(xi) Force of the storm

The storm that occurred at Dundee on the night of 28 December was recorded on board the *Mars* training ship, lying near Newport, as being of the force of 10 to 11 of the Beaufort scale, and was especially characterised by strong gusts at intervals. The evidences of wind force in the town of Dundee were not, however, such as to point to extreme wind pressure, but from the configuration of the land the main force of the gusts would probably take the line of the river.

(xii) Indications of weakness

The first indication of weakness in the bridge itself was the loosening of a number of the ties of the cross-bracing, a fact observed by the inspector, Henry Noble, in October 1878. He did not communicate this fact to Sir T. Bouch, but procured iron and packed the gibs and cotters, using for this purpose more than 100 iron packings about one-quarter or three-eighths of an inch thick, in different parts of the bridge.

All the evidence relative to the condition of the ties states that they were, to all appearance, in proper order at the date of inspection by General Hutchinson, on 25, 26 and 27 February 1878. The loosening that subsequently ensued must have resulted from lateral action, and was most probably due, as Sir T. Bouch suggested, to strains upon the cross-bracing produced by storms of wind.

Sir Thomas Bouch considers that the loosening arose from the bending of the pins in the holes, which had been left conical in casting the lugs, and it was, we think, one of the causes; but the small bearing surfaces between the gibs and cotters, and the tie-bars, only about 0.375 square inches, would tend to increase this effect, and it might have been further increased by displacement or movement at the ends of those struts where the fitting was imperfect.

Again, in October 1879, four of the columns were ascertained by Mr Noble to be cracked with vertical cracks, two of them being in the northern part of the bridge still standing, and one in pier No 38 under the high girders. The inspector (Noble) bound these columns round with wrought-iron bands, and communicated this fact to Sir Thomas Bouch, who came to the work and, in reference to other indications of straining pointed out by the inspector, decided to have extra bracings made for the curved part of the bridge north of the large girders. It has been already mentioned that the columns of the whole bridge were filled after their erection with Portland cement concrete put in from the top, and concrete of this material, unless carefully managed, is liable to swell in setting; from this circumstance, and from the unequal contraction of cast-iron and concrete by cold, internal strains might have arisen sufficient to have produced such cracks. Cracks of a like character have occurred in other viaducts; and when the fracture is vertical, it is capable of remedy, to a considerable extent, by hooping with wrought-iron bands.

In this state of the columns and ties, the storm of 28 December 1879 occurred, which would necessarily produce great tension on the ties, varying as the heavy gusts bore upon different parts of the bridge; and when, under these strains, the train came on the viaduct bringing a larger surface of wind pressure to bear, as well as increased weight on the piers, and accompanied by the jarring action due to its motion along the rails, the final catastrophe occurred.

The distance at which the girders were found from the piers and the position of the wreckage on the piers is such as would result from a fracture and separation taking place in the piers somewhere above the base of the columns; and such a fracture might have arisen from two causes: firstly, by the yielding of the cross-bracing and the consequent distortion of the form of the piers, which would throw unequal strains on the flanges and connecting bolts; or, secondly, fracture might have taken place in one of the outer leeward columns from causes similar to those which produced the fractures found in other columns shortly before the accident.

(xiii) Opinions as to the cause of the accident

Sir Thomas Bouch states it to be his opinion that the accident was occasioned by the overturning of the 2nd Class carriage and the van behind it by the force of the wind, that they were canted over against the girder, and that the force of the blow given by these vehicles at the speed at which they were travelling was sufficient to destroy portions of the girders, and so occasioned the fall. But in this opinion we do not concur, and do not consider that it is supported by the evidence of the Engineers who were called on the part of the Railway Company, Sir T. Bouch and the Contractors.

Dr Pole, Mr Stewart, and Mr Baker, all of whom were called on behalf of Sir T. Bouch, although they suggest the possibility of some shock acting in addition to the wind pressure, all concur in attributing the first failure to the lugs of the cross-bracing. Mr Cochrane believes that if the columns had been strongly braced, strongly fitted, and strongly held down by holding-down bolts, the pier would have been standing now, and adds, 'It is a question of cross-bracing, of course.' Mr Law also considers that the structure yielded because the ties were inadequate.

Conclusions arrived at by the Court

Such being the nature of the case brought under our consideration in this inquiry, we have to state as our opinion:

1st   That there is nothing to indicate any movement or settlement as having taken place in the foundations of the piers which fell.

2nd   That the wrought-iron employed was of fair strength though not of high quality as regards toughness.

3rd   That the cast-iron was also fairly good in strength, but sluggish when melted, and presented difficulty in obtaining sound castings.

4th   That the girders which have fallen were of sufficient strength, and had been carefully studied in proportioning the several parts to the duty they had to perform; in these girders, some imperfections of workmanship were found, but they were not of a character which contributed to the accident, and the fractures found in these girders were, we think, all caused by the fall from the tops of the piers.

5th   That the iron piers used in place of the brick piers originally contemplated were strong enough for supporting the vertical weight but were not of a sufficiently substantial character to sustain at so great a height girders of such magnitude as those which fell.
That the cross-bracings and fastenings were too weak to resist the lateral action of heavy gales of wind.

6th   That the workmanship and fitting of the several parts comprising the piers were inferior in many respects.

7th   That although a large staff of assistants and inspectors was employed, we consider that a sufficiently strict supervision was not exercised during the construction of that part of the work made at the Wormit Foundry. We think that the great inequality of thickness in some of the columns, the conical holes cast in the lugs, and several imperfections of workmanship which have been ascertained by this inquiry, ought to have been prevented

8th That he arrangements for the supervision of the bridge after its completion were not satisfactory, in as much as it was entrusted solely to Henry Noble, who, although an intelligent man and very competent in the class of work to which he had been accustomed, possessed no experience in structures of iron work; nor does it appear he received any definite instruction to report as to the state of the iron work of the bridge

9th That Henry Noble, having become aware that many of the ties of the cross-bracings were loosened in October 1878 ought at once to have informed Sir T. Bouch of this circumstance. Had he done so, there would have been ample time to put in stronger ties and fastenings before the occurrence of the storm which overthrew the bridge.

10th That the ties of the cross-bracing had been tightened up and brought to their bearing before the date of the inspection by General Hutchinson, and the fact that so many of them became loose so soon afterwards was an evidence of weakness in this part of the structure, and of a departure from the proper inclination or batter of the columns where it occurred; and we think that the loosening of the ties to an extent sufficient to permit of the insertion of pieces of iron one-quarter or three-eighths of an inch thick indicated a considerable change in the form of the piers, and rendered it doubtful if the piers could have recovered their form when the wind action ceased. The employment of packing pieces under such circumstances might have had the effect of fixing the parts of the structure where they were applied in their distorted form.

11th That notwithstanding the recommendation of General Hutchinson that the speed of the trains on the bridge should be restricted to 25mph, the railway company did not enforce that recommendation, and much higher speeds were frequently run on portions of the bridge.

12th That the fall of the bridge was occasioned by the insufficiently of the cross-bracing, and its fastening to sustain the force of the gale on the night of 28 December 1879, and that the bridge had been previously strained by other gales.

13th That although the general bearing of the evidence indicates the cross-bracing as being the first part to yield, yet it is possible that the fall of the bridge may have been occasioned by a fracture or partial fracture in one of the outward leeward columns produced by causes analogous to those which fractured other columns shortly before the accident; for if a fracture or partial fracture of a dangerous character occurred in one of these columns the extra strain brought on by the force of the gale accompanied by the weight and the tremor of the train might have led to its final rupture.

14th That the first, or southern, set of continuous girders covering five spans was the first that fell after the engine and part of the train had crossed the fourth pier, and that the two consecutive sets of continuous girders – each covering four spans – were in succession pulled off the piers on which their northern ends rested by the action of the first set of continuous girders falling over, and probably breaking some of the supporting columns.

15th That the extent of the work which fell must be attributed to the employment of long, continuous girders supported by piers built up of a series of cast-iron columns of the dimensions used.

In conclusion, we have to state that there is no requirement issued by the Board of Trade respecting wind pressure, and there does not appear to be any understood rule in the engineering profession regarding wind pressure in railway structures; and we therefore recommend that the Board of Trade should take such steps as may be necessary for the establishment of rules for this purpose.

We also recommend before any steps are taken for the reconstruction of the Tay Bridge that a careful examination should be made of those parts of the structure left standing, especially as regards the piers, with a view to ensuring such alterations and amendments as may be necessary to give to these portions of the work complete stability. And we transmit herewith a further report from Mr Law on that subject.

We have the honour to be, Sir, your most obedient servants

Henry Rothery
W. Yolland
W. H. Barlow

APPENDIX 2
DESCRIPTION OF
THE TAY BRIDGE

by Major General Charles Hutchinson,
the Board of Trade Inspector of Railways,
as submitted to the Court of Inquiry

Major General Charles Scrope Hutchinson was the Board of Trade's inspector of railways who inspected the Tay Bridge in order to certify that it was fit for the purposes for which it was being constructed. He described the bridge to the Court of Inquiry, and set out its length, carrying a single line of rails, as 3,450 yards. It consisted of 85 spans. All but one of the girders were built as lattice girders, the exception being a bow-string girder of 166 feet.

Eleven of the lattice girders had a span of 245 feet each; two were 227 feet each; one was 162.8 feet; 13 were 145 feet; 10 were 129.25 feet; 11 were 129 feet; and 2 were 87 feet. A further 24 spans were 67.5 feet; three were 67 feet; and one was 66.7 feet. Then came six spans of 28.9 feet, again with lattice girders.

The total dimensions of the bridge were 85 spans, in addition to which there was, adjoining the north end of the bridge, one span of 100 feet with bow-string girders and three plate girders with a span of 29 feet each.

In the 15 spans exceeding 145 feet, and with the 100-foot bow-string girders, wrought-iron cross-girders had been employed; for the other spans, cross-girders of timber were used.

Hutchinson went on that in the 13 spans of 227 feet and upwards, and in the bow-string girder spans, the roadway was carried on the bottom booms of the girders, in the other spans on the tops of the girders.

The girders were arranged in continuous groups, generally of four, five or six each, with proper provision for expansion, supported on piers of varied construction. The foundation in all cases was formed of iron cylinders lined with brickwork and concrete. Counting from the south end:

Piers 1 to 14 were entirely of brick in cement; piers 15 to 48 were brick for 5 feet above high-water mark, finished with a last one belting, upon which were carried groups of cast-iron columns braced together.

Piers 49 to 77 consisted of groups of cast-iron columns braced together, starting from the cylinders, and encased in brickwork to a height of 5 feet above high-water mark.

Piers 78 and 79 were cast-iron cylinders throughout, filled with concrete; piers 80 to 84 were cast-iron columns; piers 85 to 89 were of brick in cement.

The greatest height from the level of the rails to the high-water mark, spring tides, was 92 feet. This occurred at the centre of the large spans, from where towards the north side there was a sharply falling gradient of 1 in 74, with a gentler fall towards the south end. At each end of the bridge there were curves of 20 chains radius (a chain is 22 yards).

The permanent way consisted of double-headed rails, fished at the joints, in 24 feet lengths, weighing 75lb to the yard, secured by oak keys in cast-iron chairs weighing 80lb each, fixed at 3-feet average intervals to longitudinal timbers 17 inches wide, and varying in depth from 7 to 14 inches.

There were four spikes in each chair. Throughout the length of the bridge, each rail was provided with a guard-rail. Between the longitudinals the floor of the bridge consisted of 3-inch planking covered with a waterproof composition. A substantial hand-rail was carried along each side of the bridge.

For the purpose of adequately testing the structure, the North British Railway Company placed at Hutchinson's disposal six new goods engines, weighing 73 tons each, and each measuring 48½ feet; the total weight employed was therefore 438 tons, and the total length of engines 291 feet or, as nearly as possible, 1½ tons to the running foot.

APPENDIX 3
THE 102 WITNESSES

This appendix lists all 102 witnesses to the Tay Bridge inquiry, with their occupations or reasons for being called; for reasons of space this book does not include the evidence given by each of these witnesses.

Airy, Sir George B.	Astronomer Royal
Anderson, John	Engine driver on the Tay Bridge line
Armit, Thomas Napier	Superintended the raising of the fallen portions of the Tay Bridge
Baird, Richard	Moulder at Wormit Foundry
Baker, Benjamin	Civil engineer
Barclay, John	Diver at the wreck of the Tay Bridge
Barclay, Thomas	Signalman at the south cabin of the Tay Bridge
Barron, Peter	Witnessed the fall of the train from the bridge
Batsworth, Edward	Officer on board the training ship *Mars* stationed in the Tay
Beattie, Frank	Assistant engineer employed by contractors for the Tay Bridge
Black, John	Passenger over the Tay Bridge by the train preceding the one that fell
Bouch, Sir Thomas	Engineer of the Tay Bridge
Brand, John	Engine driver employed on the Tay Bridge line
Brunlees, James	Engineer who visited the Tay Bridge after the fall at the request of the North British Railway Company
Buick, John	Passenger over the Tay Bridge by the train preceding the one that fell
Camphuis, Gerrit Willem	Assistant engineer employed by the contractors for the Tay Bridge works
Clark, Charles	Kept a weather record at Dundee
Clark, George	Saw the train on the Tay Bridge before its fall
Clark, William Abercrombie	Saw the train on the Tay Bridge before its fall
Coburn, Elijah	Tap and dye maker, employed by the Cleveland Nut & Bolt Company upon bolts for the Tay Bridge
Coburn, junior, Elijah	Tap and dye maker, employed by the Cleveland Nut & Bolt Company upon bolts for the Tay Bridge
Cochrane, John	Engineer who visited the Tay Bridge after its fall at the request of the North British Railway Company

Coutts, William	Engine driver employed on the Tay Bridge line
Cocks, John	Diver employed at the wreck of the Tay Bridge
Dale, David	Painter employed on the Tay Bridge
Dewey, Henry	Diver employed at the raising of the sunken girders of the Tay Bridge
Dixon, William	Employed to rivet girder junctions and to overhaul the bolting of the columns at the Tay Bridge
Donegany, Peter	Painter employed on the Tay Bridge
Dougall, Admiral W. H. M.	Observed from his house the storm during which the Tay Bridge was destroyed
Drummond, Dugald	Locomotive Superintendent of the North British Railway Company
Duncan, William	Guard employed on the Tay Bridge line
Evans, John	Painter employed on the Tay Bridge
Fender, George	Turner employed at Wormit Foundry
Ferguson, Fergus	Foreman moulder at Wormit Foundry
Foreman, Andrew	Moulder at Wormit Foundry
Friend, William	Collected tickets at St Fort station from the passengers in the train that went down
Gibb, John	Dresser employed at Wormit foundry
Gilkes, Edgar	Partner in the firm of contractors for the erection of the Tay Bridge
Gourlay, Henry	Spoke to the witness Barron after he had seen the train fall from the bridge
Gowan, George	Moulder at Wormit Foundry
Gray, John	Diver employed at the wreck of the Tay Bridge
Gray, John	Painter employed on the Tay Bridge
Greig, Capt John	Lighthouse-keeper at Dundee
Gröthe, Albert	Resident engineer in the employ of the contractors for the Tay Bridge works
Grubb, Rev George	Passenger over the Tay Bridge by the train preceding the one that fell
Hadland, James Francis	Clerk to the Cleveland Nut & Bolt Company, who made bolts for the Tay Bridge
Hall, Thomas	Bolt-maker in the employ of the Cleveland Nut & Bolt Company
Hampton, Alexander	Moulder at Wormit Foundry
Harley, Peter	Diver employed at the wreck of the Tay Bridge
Himsley, George	Nut-maker in the employ of the Cleveland Nut & Bolt Company
Hume, George Thomas	Daily passenger by Tay Bridge trains
Hutchinson, Major-General Charles Scrope	Inspector of the Tay Bridge on behalf of the Board of Trade before it opened
Hutchinson, Alexander	Passenger by Tay Bridge trains
Hutton, David	Moulder at Wormit Foundry
Ingles, Alexander	Collected tickets at St Fort station from the passengers in the train that went down

Jack, John	Observed from his house at Newport the storm during which the bridge was destroyed
Kennedy, Alexander	Engine driver of the last train that crossed the Tay Bridge
Law, Henry	Engineer appointed by the Court of Inquiry to inspect and report on the fallen bridge
Lawson, James Black	Witnessed the fall of the train
Leng, John	Editor of the *Dundee Advertiser* and a daily passenger by Tay Bridge trains
McBeath, George	Inspected the ironwork of the Tay Bridge after its completion on behalf of Sir Thomas Bouch
McDonald, Duncan	Passenger by Tay Bridge trains
McGovan, Edward	Superintended the bolting of the columns and the tie-bars of the Tay Bridge
McGowan, James	Moulder at Wormit Foundry
McKelvie, William Ross	Keeper of a weather record at Dundee for the Scottish Meteorological Society
McLaren, James	Passenger by Tay Bridge trains
McMahon, Hugh	Seaman on ship *Mars* stationed in the Tay
Mason, Thomas	Bolt-maker in the employ of the Cleveland Nut & Bolt Company
Maxwell, junior, Alexander	Witnessed the fall of the train from the bridge
Meik, Charles	Assistant to Sir Thomas Bouch
Miller, Dr James	Passenger by Tay Bridge trains
Miller, Robert	Moulder at Wormit Foundry
Milne, Alexander	Dresser at Wormit Foundry
Milne, John	Painter employed on the Tay Bridge
Morris, Robert	Station Master at St Fort station
Moyes, James	Locomotive foreman in the employ of the North British Railway Company
Murray, George	Inspector of the line on the Tay Bridge
Nelson, John	Painter employed on the Tay Bridge
Newcombe, William	Foreman erector of the high girders of the Tay Bridge
Noble, Henry Abel	Inspector of the Tay Bridge in the employ of the North British Railway Company
Norley, William	Diver employed at the wreck of the Tay Bridge
Oram, William	Riveter employed on the girder junctions of the Tay Bridge
Pirie, David	Examined the Tay Bridge with a view to contracting for the painting
Pole, Dr William, FRS	In conjunction with Allan Stewart supplied information required of the North British Railway Company by the Court of Inquiry
Quosbarth, Herman	Passenger by Tay Bridge trains
Ramsay, Alexander	Guard on the Tay Bridge line
Reeves, Frederick William	Assistant engineer employed by contractors for the Tay Bridge works
Roberts, James	Locomotive foreman
Robertson, Henry	Passenger by Tay Bridge trains

Robertson, John	Employed at the raising of the sunken girders of the Tay Bridge
Robertson, Peter	Painter employed on the Tay Bridge
Robertson, William	Harbour-master at Dundee, ex-Provost and passenger on Tay Bridge trains
Robertson, William	Carriage and wagon inspector in the employ of the North British Railway Company, who saw the train enter the bridge
Scott, Capt	Superintendent of the training ship *Mars* stationed in the Tay
Scott, Robert Henry, FRS	Secretary to the Meteorological Council
Shand, Robert	Guard of the last train that crossed the Tay Bridge
Simpson, Edward	Diver employed at the wreck of the Tay Bridge
Smith, James	Station Master at the Taybridge station, Dundee
Somerville, Henry	Signalman at the north end of the Tay Bridge
Steward, Alexander	Joiner, who made the case for the Newport Water Pipe on the Tay Bridge
Stewart, Allan D.	Engineer who assisted Sir Thomas Bouch in the calculations for the Tay Bridge and, with Dr Pole, furnished information required of the North British Railway Company by the Court of Inquiry
Watt, John	Surfaceman for North British Railway Company

BIBLIOGRAPHY

Report of the Committee of Inquiry upon the circumstances attending the fall of the Tay Bridge on 28th December 1879 (Parliamentary Papers, Vol xxxix, 1880)

Brunel, Isambard Kingdom *Reports to the Board of the Great Western Railway* (Public Record Office, RAIL250\82)

Buchan, A. *The Tay Bridge Storm, 28th December 1879 (Journal of the Scottish Meteorological Society*, Vol 5, 1876-1880)

Drummond, Dugald *Locomotives of the North British Railway*

Lewis, Peter R. *The Beautiful Bridge of the Silvery Tay* (Stroud, 2005)

McKean, Charles *Battle for the North* (London, 2006)

Martin, T. J. and MacLeod, I. A. *The Tay Railway Bridge Disaster: A reappraisal based on modern analysis methods* (Proceedings, Institution of Civil Engineers, 1995)

Nicoll, Murray, Nicoll, Claire and Buttars, Grant *Victims of the Tay Bridge Disaster of Sunday 28 December 1879* (Tay Valley Family History Society, 2005)

Simmons, Jack and Biddle, Gordon *Oxford Companion to British Railway History* (Oxford, 1997)

Swinfen, David *The Fall of the Tay Bridge* (Edinburgh, 1998)

INDEX